CROSS THE GOLDEN RIVER

COORDINATING AUTHOR

JACK BOOTH

DAVID BOOTH

JO PHENIX & LARRY SWARTZ

I M P R E S S I O N S

HOLT, RINEHART AND WINSTON OF CANADA, LIMITED

Executive Editor: Wendy Cochran
Developmental Editor: Grant Heckman
Editorial Assistant: Christine McGarity
Production Editor: Elizabeth Reid
Art Director: Mary Opper
Designers: Martin Gould, Sandra Quigley
Cover Illustrator: Doug Martin

ISBN: 0-03-921901-1

Canadian Cataloguing in Publication Data

Main entry under title:
Cross the golden river

(Impressions)
For use in schools.
ISBN 0-03-921901-1

I. Readers (Elementary). I. Booth, Jack, 1946-
II. Series: Impression (Toronto, Ont.)

PE1119.C76 1986   428.6   C86-093582-5

Illustrations
Victor Gad: pp. 6-7; *Gerald Rose:* pp. 8-13; *James Marshall:* pp. 14-23; *Ken Stampnick:* pp. 24-27; *Joanne Fitzgerald:* pp. 28-29, 118-121; *Patti Stren:* pp. 30-40; *Martine Gourbault:* pp. 41-47, 222-230; *Laurie LaFrance:* pp. 48-49, 182-183; *Frank Hammond:* pp. 50-53, 162-165, 231; *Wendy Wortsman:* pp. 54-55; *John Heinly:* pp. 56-69; *San Murata:* pp. 68-69, 196-199; *Tom Hunt:* pp. 70-71, 142-147; *Shelley Browning:* pp. 73, 77; *Sheila Armstrong:* pp. 80-85; *Jeff Pickerman:* pp. 86-87; *Barbara Klunder:* pp. 88-91, 232-233; *Paul Galdone:* pp. 92-95; *Quentin Blake:* pp. 96-107; *Wojtek Gorczynski:* pp. 108-109; *Mischa Richter:* pp. 110-117; *William Kimber:* pp. 122-123, 286-287; *Allen Shugar:* pp. 124-125; *Michael Foreman:* pp. 126-133; *Ul de Rico:* pp. 134-139; *Jamie Bennet:* pp. 140-141; *Jock MacRae:* pp. 148-149; *Richard daMota:* pp. 150-161; *Chris Van Allsburg:* pp. 166-175; *Magda Markowski:* pp. 176-181; *Kellie Jobson:* pp. 184-185; *Tina Holdcroft:* pp. 186-191; *Victoria Chess:* pp. 192-195; *Helen Mariancou:* pp. 200-211; *Aliki:* pp. 212-215; *Tina Seemann:* pp. 216-219; *Peter Parnall:* pp. 246-253; *Kuzo Shimizu:* pp. 256-260; *Vladyana Krykorka:* pp. 254-255; *Ken Nutt:* pp. 261-265; *Jeff Jackson:* pp. 266-269; *Glen Loates:* pp. 270-273; *Michael Reinhart:* pp. 274-285; *Martin Gould:* p. 75, from an original by Shelley Browning.

The authors and publishers gratefully acknowledge the educators listed below for their contribution to the development of this program:
Ron Benson   *Coordinator of Primary Education   Scarborough Board of Education*
Ethel Buchanan   *Language Arts Consultant   Winnipeg, Manitoba*
Margaret Crocker   *Teacher and Vice Principal   Bedford District School Board, Halifax County*
William Fagan   *Language Arts Coordinator   Roman Catholic School Board for St. John's, Newfoundland*
Ruth Fulton   *Supervisor of Elementary Education   District No. 20, Saint John, New Brunswick*
June Gravel   *Language Arts Coordinator   Dufferin-Peel Roman Catholic Separate School Board*
Pat Hogan   *Language Arts Consultant   Calgary Board of Education Coordinator Calgary Writing Project*
Margaret Joyce   *Language Arts Consultant   School Unit No. 3, Charlottetown, P.E.I.*
Linda Kaser   *Coordinator, Language Arts and English K-12   Richmond School District*
Roberta McKay   *Consultant, Language Arts/ Social Studies   Edmonton Public Schools*
Ina Mary Rutherford   *Supervisor of Reading and Primary Education   Bruce County Board of Education*
Janice Petracek   *Executive Assistant to the Deputy Director of Education   Regina School Division*

Printed in Canada   3 4 5   90 89 88 87

TABLE OF CONTENTS

Humour Is a Marvellous Invention

We all enjoy reading stories and poems that make us laugh: sometimes with out-loud laughter, and sometimes with silent, inside laughter. What strikes you as funny? Do you like to read about strange situations or people who are doing funny things? Would you rather see families in books who look and act like people you know, or people who are exaggerated like cartoons? Often people laugh at things when they are in special moods. For example, if you have had a difficult day, you may want to read a story that takes you far away from where you live, into a world that makes you forget your troubles. Or when you are in a very silly mood, you might look for a poem or a song that is fun to say or sing. Do you ever just giggle at the words in front of you, saying them again and again and laughing every time? Or do you enjoy looking at the pictures that accompany a story, to see what the artist thinks is funny?

Do you think that the inventor in this selection was trying to be funny?

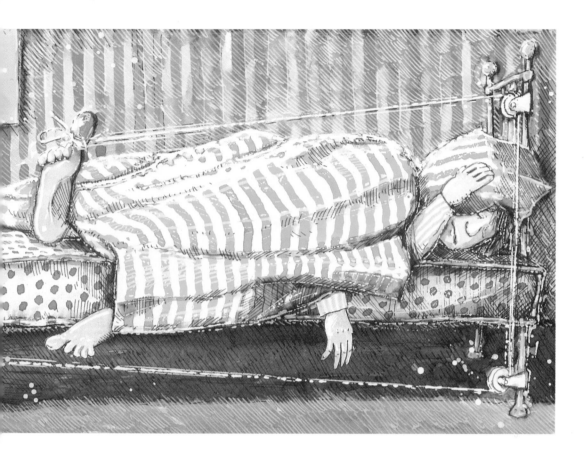

Alvin awoke with a start the instant the string jerked his big toe. Quickly, he reached down and turned off the alarm clock before his toe turned purple.

Each morning a jerk on his big toe woke up Alvin Fernald. Alvin was a great inventor, and the string was one of his inventions. It ran to an alarm clock which he had bolted to the foot of his bed. He had removed the alarm bell so it wouldn't wake his parents. When the alarm went off each morning it wound up a string which was tied to his big toe. Sometimes the toe became purple before he could turn off the alarm, but otherwise the Silent Waker Upper worked fine.

(from *The Marvellous Inventions of Alvin Fernald*, by C.B. Hicks)

It might be fun to have Alvin for a friend, don't you think?

What's so funny? The stories and poems in this section! Jump into the funny waters that lie ahead. And remember, you are allowed to laugh—sometimes out loud, and sometimes inside your heart.

THE TIGER-SKIN RUG

by Gerald Rose

There was once a very thin tiger, who lived on the edge of the jungle. He was sad and thin because he was getting old and food was difficult to catch. The monkeys threw nuts at him and called him names.

At night he would gaze at the Rajah's palace and sometimes he would look in the windows as the Rajah and his family ate their food in warmth and comfort. He wished that he could join their friendly company.

One day he was watching a servant beating the rugs in the palace gardens. One of the old rugs was a tiger-skin.

The tiger had an idea. While the servant's back was turned, he jumped over the wall, took down the old tiger-skin rug, hid it under a bush and draped himself over the line.

The servant continued with his beating and beat poor Tiger even harder than the rest of the rugs, because he looked so dirty and moth-eaten.

Finally, when there was not a speck of dust left, the servant carried all the rugs back into the palace and spread them about in their correct places.

Tiger was put in the dining hall.

Soon the Rajah and his family came in to have their evening meal. They laughed and ate and talked and Tiger was glad to be in their company. They did not notice him, for he looked thin and moth-eaten, just like the old tiger-skin rug which they were used to.

After the meal, when they had all left the room, Tiger jumped up and finished all the scraps. Then he drank some tea and lay down for a good night's sleep.

This was a wonderful life and he was determined not to spoil it. Every day he enjoyed the family's company. Every evening he finished the scraps and drank some tea . . . but he was careful to keep very still whenever anyone came into the room.

At first nobody suspected that he was not the real tiger-skin rug, because he was so thin and looked so moth-eaten. The Rajah would play and frighten the children with him. The children would pretend he was a real live tiger.

But Tiger was worried, because he knew that he was not as thin as he used to be, or as moth-eaten.

One day the Rajah said: "How strange—the old tiger-skin rug has improved with age. But it really is beginning to smell. If it cannot be cleaned it will have to go."

The following day the tiger was taken out into the garden and scrubbed with an old broom. The soap made his eyes sting. Then he was left on the line in the hot sun to drip and dry.

When the servant carried Tiger back to the dining hall he complained that either the tiger-skin rug was getting heavier or he was getting older and weaker.

That night the tiger did not eat any scraps, and he could not sleep. He knew that he would soon be found out and perhaps made into a real tiger-skin rug. Whatever could he do?

Suddenly he heard a noise. All the hairs on his spine stood on end and the end of his tail twitched.

Three robbers were climbing in through the window.

They were carrying a sack and they began to fill it with silver dishes, ornaments and anything of value.

While Tiger was wondering what to do the door burst open and the Rajah rushed in. The robbers knocked him down, and drew out wicked knives.

Then Tiger stood up and roared. The roar echoed down every corridor and round every room and across the palace gardens, waking everybody.

Tiger leapt to the Rajah's rescue.

The three robbers took flight. They were in such a hurry that they became stuck in the window as they fought to get through all at once.

When the Rajah had recovered from his shock and his family and his servants had gathered, the Rajah proclaimed:

"The tiger-skin rug has saved us. He must stay forever."
And so he did.

He was never beaten and scrubbed again, but instead he bathed in the garden pool. He went on picnics with the family and rode on elephants. The children played with him and the Rajah's wives loved him.

He no longer ate scraps. He had his own plate of food and his own bowl of the best Indian tea.

In the evening he lay on the floor with the family around him, for he was still their tiger-skin rug—a real tiger-skin rug and the best in the whole world.

DINNER AT ALBERTA'S

by Russell Hoban

"Arthur," said Mrs. Crocodile to her son one evening at dinner, "you are eating like a regular little beast."

"He won't close his mouth when he chews," said Arthur's sister, Emma, "and I have to sit across from him, so I have a good view of everything."

"Whuzzhuh maher?" said Arthur.

"Don't talk when your mouth is full," said Father. "Little bits of ravioli are landing on your sister and no one can understand what you are saying."

"It's awful," said Emma.

"It certainly is," said Mother.

"Everybody always picks on me," said Arthur when his mouth was empty.

"Look," said Emma, "now he is feeling the saltshaker."

"Don't feel the saltshaker, Arthur," said Father. "Either take some salt or leave it alone."

"My goodness," said Arthur, "dinner around here is no fun if everybody is going to pick on me," and he began to diddle with his spoon.

"Arthur is diddling with his spoon," said Emma.

"Emma," said Father, "you do not have to report everything to me. I am sitting right here and I can see perfectly well."

"Arthur has no manners," said Emma.

"Why does everybody pester me so much?" said Arthur. And he left the table without excusing himself and played his electric guitar very loudly in his room.

"Between his table manners and his electric guitar that boy will destroy the world," said Mother.

"Maybe the world will get him first," said Emma, and she excused herself and went to clean the tomato sauce off her dress.

The next morning on the way to the office Mr. Crocodile told

his friend John Hippopotamus about it.

"One way or another, boys are trouble," said John. "Take my sons, for instance. They seem to think that just because we live at the bottom of the river they can track mud all over the living room."

"That's shocking," said Mr. Crocodile.

"It is," said John Hippopotamus, "but my boys have beautiful table manners, as far as that goes."

Then they both read their newspapers.

That evening at dinner Arthur chewed with his mouth open, felt the saltshaker, and diddled with his spoon again. He also knocked over the milk pitcher while reaching for the beef stroganoff instead of asking Father to pass it. Then Arthur wiped up the milk with a sponge, dropped the sponge into the beef stroganoff, was sent to finish dinner in his room, tripped over his music stand, cleaned the beef stroganoff off the rug, and played his electric guitar very loudly, very late.

The next afternoon Mrs. Crocodile went shopping with her friend Minnie Boa.

"What am I going to do with that boy?" Mrs. Crocodile asked Minnie.

"It's hard to say," said Minnie. "We eat only once every two weeks, so it isn't too bad at our place. But my children are terrible squeezers. We haven't got a whole piece of china or crockery in the house, and nobody will play with them anymore. Broken ribs all over town."

"I suppose we all have our troubles," said Mrs. Crocodile, and both ladies bought new hats.

The next day after school Emma brought home a friend, Alberta Saurian. Alberta was very pretty, and when Arthur saw her he brought out his guitar and his amplifier and played very fancy music very fast.

"This is my brother, Arthur," said Emma to Alberta.

"How do you do," said Alberta.

Arthur nodded and played faster. They could not hear him above the noise that came out of his amplifier, but they saw his mouth say, "Hi."

"He's nice," said Alberta to Emma.

"He's very sincere," said Emma.

When Emma asked if Alberta could stay for dinner, Mrs. Crocodile was not sure about it. "You know why," she said to Emma.

"I know," said Emma. "But people are going to have to find out about Arthur sooner or later. We can't lock him up. Can we?"

"No," said Mother. "We can't."

"Then we'll just have to take our chances," said Emma, and she and Alberta set the table.

At dinner Arthur stared at Alberta for a long time and did not eat.

"Arthur likes you," Emma whispered to her friend.

"He's very shy and polite, isn't he?" said Alberta.

"Eat something, Arthur," said Father. "You haven't touched your food."

"I guess I'm not hungry," said Arthur, and he picked at his cauliflower. Arthur mostly ate bread and butter and drank milk that Father poured for him. He watched to see how Alberta took a little butter from the butter dish and put it on her plate; then he did the same. When she broke off a piece of bread and buttered it, he did it the way she did, and he smiled at her.

After Alberta went home Father said, "For once dinner was a pleasure. Alberta should come here every night."

"Arthur would starve," said Mother.

"Everybody always pesters me," said Arthur, and he went to his room. He had Oreo cookies and malted-milk balls there, and he ate them all up.

The next day Arthur said to Emma, "When is your friend what's-her-name coming around again?"

"Who?" said Emma. "Alberta?"

"Yes," said Arthur, "Alberta."

"I don't know," said Emma. "Why?"

"No reason," said Arthur, and he played his guitar.

"What are you playing?" said Emma. "I never heard that one before."

"Just something I'm fooling around with," said Arthur. "Something I made up." And he blushed.

"Oho," said Emma. And the next time she saw Alberta she said, "Arthur is making up a song for you."

"Arthur is really adorable," said Alberta.

"I never thought of him that way," said Emma.

"He really is," said Alberta, "and I am going to ask my mother if I can invite you and him to dinner at our house tomorrow."

"We'll need a little time," said Emma. "Could you make it next week?"

"All right," said Alberta. "Let's make it next Tuesday."

When Emma went home she told Arthur.

"Oh boy," said Arthur, and he turned up his amplifier.

At dinner that evening Arthur partly closed his mouth when he chewed.

"All the way, Arthur," said Father. Arthur closed his mouth all the way.

"Don't hunch over your food as if you were crouching to spring," said Mother. "It won't get away from you." Arthur stopped hunching over.

"The fork, Arthur," said Emma. "Watch how I hold it. Don't make a fist like that." Arthur watched how Emma held her fork.

"Howmaydays wegot?" he said to Emma.

"Not with your mouth full," said Emma "We have five more days. Lots of time."

Every evening Arthur practised eating the way Mother and Father and Emma did, and for every dinner Mother cooked different things for him to practise on. On Monday night she said, "I ought to have a cheese fondue instead of flounder. If they have a fondue tomorrow he's going to be in trouble."

"Arthur," said Father, "don't ball up your napkin in your left hand like that."

"Too many things to think about," said Arthur. He was breathing hard.

"Relax," said Father. "Listen to how Emma breathes."

"Too much," said Arthur, letting out his breath. "What's the good of it all?"

"All right," said Father. "Forget it. Just eat at Alberta's the way you eat at home, and let it go at that."

Arthur breathed like Emma.

"That's it," said Father to Mother. "This is a turning point."

On Tuesday afternoon Mother made Arthur take a shower and put on clean clothes after school.

"I took a shower Sunday night," said Arthur. "What do I need a shower for?"

"Why did you make up a song for Alberta?" said Mother. "You wanted to be nice to her, right?"

"I guess so," said Arthur.

"So smell nice too," said Mother.

When Arthur and Emma were ready to go, they rowed over to Alberta's house. Mrs. Saurian and Emma had met before, and Alberta introduced Arthur to her mother.

"Mother," she said, "this is Arthur Crocodile."

"How do you do, Arthur," said Mrs. Saurian. "I've heard so much about you."

"How do you do, Mrs. Saurian," said Arthur. Mrs. Saurian put out her hand and Arthur shook it. He had practised that with Emma and his mother.

"This is my brother, Sidney," said Alberta.

"How do you do," said Arthur.

"Hi," said Sidney. They shook hands. Sidney got a better grip than Arthur and he squeezed hard. Then Arthur was introduced to Alberta's sister, Marilyn, and when Alberta's father came home he was introduced to him.

Then they all sat down at the table. Mrs. Saurian had cooked flounder.

"Oh boy," said Arthur, "I know this one . . . "

" . . . is going to be delicious," said Emma. "We both love flounder."

"I'm so glad," said Mrs. Saurian. "We're all very fond of it too."

Arthur was careful not to spill anything. When he wanted potatoes he said, "Please pass the potatoes." He used breath control and he did not hunch over. He kept his mouth closed when he chewed, kept his napkin in his lap, and used his knife and fork the right way. Arthur noticed that Sidney ate mostly bread and butter and drank milk.

Sidney watched how Arthur took butter from the butter dish and how he buttered his bread, and he did it the same way. Arthur smiled at Sidney, and Sidney made words with his mouth without saying them out loud.

"Never mind that, Sidney," said Mr. Saurian. "You just watch how Arthur eats, and maybe you can learn some manners."

When his father was not looking, Sidney said to Arthur with his mouth but not out loud, "I'll get you later."

"Any time," Arthur said back the same way.

Arthur did everything right at dinner, and he talked too, when his mouth had nothing in it.

"I hear you made up a song," said Alberta.

"Yes," said Arthur.

"That's wonderful," said Mr. Saurian. "That's a real gift, to be able to do that." Sidney made more words with his mouth.

After dinner they went into the living room and Arthur plugged in his amplifier and guitar.

"Tell us the name of your song, Arthur," said Mrs. Saurian.

"Well, it is not exactly a song because it does not have any words," said Arthur, "and it is called *Alberta*."

"Oh boy," said Sidney, and he let his head flop over and rolled his eyes.

"I think that is very sweet, Arthur," said Mrs. Saurian.

Alberta blushed.

Arthur played his song with a lot of tremolo. All the Saurians clapped and cheered, and Arthur bowed.

"That was very, very pretty," said Mrs. Saurian. "Really lovely."

"Thank you," said Arthur, loosening his necktie a little. "That is why it is called *Alberta*."

"Oho!" said Mr. Saurian, and Alberta blushed again.

"Well," said Emma, "I think we should be going now."

"Stay a little longer," said Mrs. Saurian. "I'm so pleased that Alberta has found such nice friends."

"Come on back to my room," said Alberta to Emma.

"Come on outside," said Sidney to Arthur, "and I'll show you my tree house."

"Fine," said Arthur.

When Arthur and Sidney came back their clothes were mussed up and dirty, and Sidney had a puffed-up lip.

"I bumped into a branch," said Sidney. Mr. Saurian lifted his eyebrows and nodded his head slowly at Arthur, and Arthur smiled and nodded back.

Then it was time to go home. Arthur and Emma said good night and thanked the Saurians for a very pleasant evening. Arthur also thanked Sidney for showing him the tree house.

"Well," said Emma as they rowed home, "you see how nice it is to be with people when you learn some manners?"

"Yes," said Arthur, "and I think the nicest part of manners is

teaching them to other people, the way I did to Sidney."

"That's what keeps the whole thing going," said Emma.

"It sure does," said Arthur, and he whistled *Alberta* all the way home.

JOHNNY THE JUVENILE JUGGLER

by Dennis Lee

Johnny had hoops he could sling in the air
And he brought them along to the Summerhill Fair.
And a man from a carnival sideshow was there,
Who declared that he needed a juggler.

    And it's
        Oops! Johnny, whoops! Johnny,
        Swing along your hoops, Johnny,
        Spin a little pattern as you go;
          (Clap! Clap!)

    Because it's
        Oops! Johnny's hoops! Johnny,
        Sling a loop-the-loop, Johnny,
        Whoops! Johnny, oops! Johnny, O!
          (Clap! Clap!)

Well the man was astonished at how the hoops flew,
And he said, 'It's amazing what some kids can do!'
And now in the carnival, Act Number Two
Is Johnny the Juvenile Juggler

    And it's
        Oops! Johnny, whoops! Johnny,
        Swing along your hoops, Johnny,
        Spin a little pattern as you go;
          (Clap! Clap!)

Because it's
    Oops! Johnny's hoops! Johnny,
    Sling a loop-the-loop, Johnny,
    Whoops! Johnny, oops! Johnny, O!
        (Clap! Clap!)

THE BULLY

One day this kid comes up to me
And tries to act so tough—
And just because we stole his bike,
And called him shrimp and stuff!

I stood and faced him all alone.
My gang had run away.
But he was barely half my size;
I wasn't scared to stay.

You wouldn't think a little kid
Could be so tough and mean,
We fought for half an hour, although
Of course the kid got creamed.

I stuck my nose against his fist
And struck a sudden blow;
I drove my head between his knees
And wouldn't let them go;

And then, because the little creep
Had tried a trick or two,
I fell down on the grass, and bashed
my rear against his shoe.

And then I let him run away.
I knew he'd had enough.
But that's the way I handle kids
That think they're really tough!

CAN YOU CANOE?

Can you canoe
in Kalamazoo?
Can you canoe
In Kamloops?
Can you canoe
At a quarter to two
In a van when the traffic
Jam loops?

I *can* canoe
In Kalamazoo;
I *can* canoe
In Kamloops;
But I cannot canoe
At a quarter to two
In a van when the traffic
Jam loops.

(Canoe?)

Poems by Dennis Lee

OOH-AAH-EEE—IT'S DENNIS LEE!

by Melanie Zola

Who says it better than Dennis Lee?

"Suppose," Lee asks, "suppose a large green poem came and sat on your head. What would you do?

"Imagine, it's kind of enormous. And it shambles around as if it wants a biscuit, and licks your face, and winds all its handles backwards. And then it sits on your head. What would you do?"

He takes another puff on his pipe and sighs.

"Of course," he continues, "the whole thing is ridiculous. A poem that does that sort of thing is sometimes purple, or blue, or splotchy like measles, and it has those little knobs around the edge to hang onto. But it's never *green!* The idea is totally silly!

"Still, what would you do? . . . The best thing, of course, is to Just Ignore It. But then the poem starts beating its chest like one of Tarzan's apes, and chattering like a CBC commercial, and putting those rotten little claws it's got down into your brain. And it scrunches them up and stirs them around till you're half out of your mind. And *then* where are you?

"No: there is only one thing to do. If you want to get a poem out of your hair, this is how. You must write it on a piece of paper. That's write. Right it down, play with it, make it feel at home. Get it rite, get it ridden, make sure it is rote so it will never have to be wrighted again. And then it will climb off your head and leave you alone."

Here, in a few words, are the Dennis Lee formulae for kids to help them write a poem—a real poem.

"The poem I'm after takes our lives here and now in Canada, and makes them so luminous and real in words that people any-where can live in them. . . .

"While you're writing it, don't try to pretend you're anyone but the person you are. Don't use poetic-sounding words that feel phony; see if you can coax the words you know best into the poem. And don't put in feelings you don't have, just because they seem nice (or

shocking, or poetic); write with the feelings you really know—tender, angry, amused, and so forth . . . you can put anything in. But only if it tells the truth about something you know. . . .

"It's very hard. To say what's right under your nose is the hardest thing there is. . . . What I want is a poem that tells the truth about something that matters to you. Can you write that poem? I expect to spend the rest of my life trying."

Dennis Lee's crazy concoctions don't just happen. It may take as long as five years to write one book of poetry.

He writes his verses longhand, works and reworks them, types and rewrites as he goes along. A four-line poem can be the result of 30 rewrites; a longer poem may involve as many as 50 revisions.

Dennis Lee writes full time in the deep quiet of his Toronto home. His wife Linda and three children, Kevyn, Hilary and Julian just leave him to it—they know he's got another one of those large, green poems sitting on his head. And kids of all ages are waiting to have it written.

MOUNTAIN ROSE

by Patti Stren

rose's special carriage

3 gears

bumper

more bumpers

ONE

Rose was big. Even when she was a baby, Rose was so big she couldn't fit in the carriage her brother had used. Her parents, who worked in a circus, had to get a special carriage for her, one with eight wheels, three gears and bumpers.

Rose hated being big. She was so big she wore skateboards instead of roller skates. Everything about Rose was big, even the elephant-shaped birthmark on the inside of her left wrist.

When she was six, her parents died in a circus accident. Rose went to live with her Aunt Sadie, and her beloved brother was sent to live with Aunt Sarah on the West Coast.

Aunt Sadie tried to make Rose feel good about herself. She'd tell Rose she had "healthy hair" and "a lovely personality" and "would go far someday." But Rose just wanted to be like everybody else. Smaller.

TWO

Rose was the biggest kid in her class. The other kids teased her . . . saying she needed her own zip code and that she took baths in Lake Ontario.

One day she was standing alone in the school yard. She heard someone scream.

Rose wheeled around. The class bully, Roger "Toe-Jam Face" Pittsley, was pushing in Little Barney Edsel's face. Rose swung Little Barney into the air with one hand, while she held Roger in a headlock.

"I give up! Stop! Let go!" shouted Roger.

Rose winked at Little Barney. "Should we let him go?" she asked.

"Yeah, let him go," said a man's voice.

"I'm sorry, sir, I really am." Rose let Roger go. "I didn't mean to hurt him. I'm sorry."

"Cut the apologies. You're talking to Paddy Flanagan—the best high school wrestling coach in a hundred miles. I got an eye for talent. And kid, you've got TALENT."

Rose looked embarrassed. "I do?"

"You DO!!" said Paddy. "You just beat Lester B. Pearson High School's wrestling champion."

Paddy smiled. "I have plans for you."

THREE

Paddy's plans were to turn Rose into a champion wrestler. So Rose jogged to school every day. After class she ran thirty laps around the track, did thirty push-ups, thirty chin-ups, thirty sit-ups and thirty jumping jacks. After that, Paddy had her swim twenty laps in the pool—without stopping. If Paddy found Rose munching on potato chips or candy bars, he would make her do ten more laps around the track.

Rose trained like this every day—even on Saturdays! She won her high school's heavyweight title. She won her high school's regional title. She was the most promising young wrestler in Canada.

Rose felt good about herself.

FOUR

Rose graduated from high school and became a professional wrestler. Mountain Rose was her name. Paddy Flanagan was her full-time coach.

Rose beat forty-seven opponents in her first year. She beat Mirabella Will, "Tough-Talking" Tallulah, Teresa Flunk, Jane Perils, and Henrietta "Heartburn" Hardy. Lolla Lensky was the forty-seventh. Now Rose was to wrestle Desdemona Grunt, Ladies' Champion of the World.

FIVE

Rose and Paddy Flanagan had dreamed of this night. The arena was packed with Rose's classmates, her teachers and half the people in town. Rose and Desdemona came into the ring. Rose smiled. Desdemona grunted.

The ring announcer cried: "In this corner, weighing one hundred and seventy-eight pounds, the challenger . . . Mountain Rose! And in this corner, weighing in at two hundred and twelve pounds, the Ladies' Champion of the World . . . Desdemona Grunt!"

There were roars and cheers from the crowd as the referee pulled Rose and Desdemona to the centre of the ring.

"Now I want a fair match, you hear?" he told them. "When the bell rings, come out fighting."

Desdemona sneered at Mountain Rose. "You might as well quit right now, kid, 'cause everybody knows I'M the best lady wrestler in the world."

"Maybe so," laughed Rose, "but I'M the best lady wrestler in the WHOLE GALAXY."

"Oh YEAH? Well I'M the best lady wrestler IN THE WHOLE UNIVERSE!" yelled Desdemona.

"But I'M the best wrestler IN THIS RING!" Rose replied.

The referee waved his arms. "Excuse me," he said. "Is this a tea party or are you going to fight?"

"I'm not only going to fight—I'm gonna CREAM her!" said Desdemona.

"Go to your corners!" cried the referee.

"Don't let her get to you," Paddy told Rose. "And don't forget to use your flying scissor lock."

Just to be on the safe side, Rose kissed the elephant mark on the inside of her wrist. It had always brought her luck, except when she lost her parents in the circus accident and Aunt Sadie sent her beloved brother out West.

SIX

The bell rang and Rose moved to the centre of the ring.

"Hit 'er in the face, Grunt . . . Smash 'er, Rose . . . Throw 'er over your shoulder . . . " the crowd shouted.

Mountain Rose looked Desdemona straight in the eye, jumped up in the air and yelled, "YEEE-HAAAA!" in her loudest voice, wrapping her legs around Desdemona's waist and flipping her onto the floor.

Then Rose caught her with a headlock and pinned Desdemona to the mat.

"One-two-three," counted the referee. Before Desdemona could figure out what was happening, the fight was over.

The crowd screamed, "Boo! Hiss! Fix! Fix!"

The announcer came into the ring. "Ladies and gentlemen, the new Ladies' Wrestling Champion of the World . . . MOUNTAIN ROSE!"

SEVEN

Rose couldn't believe she had won. Everybody came into the ring to congratulate her, even the Men's Wrestling Champion of the World, Gardenia Gus.

"Hey, for a girl you're not bad," Gus told Mountain Rose, and shook her hand.

"What do you mean, for a girl she's not bad?" asked Flanagan, standing on his tiptoes and pushing Rose out of the way. "Why, she could beat YOU with one hand tied behind her back."

"Beat ME? Gardenia Gus, the World Champ?!"

Paddy looked him in the eye. "Are you ready to put your money where your mouth is? You don't have the nerve to fight Rose."

"Don't have the NERVE?" cried Gus. "Hey, I'll take her on right now."

"Hold it," said the referee. "I'M only being paid for one match tonight."

"We'll fight him in a week," declared Paddy. "Mountain Rose will beat the pants off him."

EIGHT

"Why'd you get me into this?" Rose asked when she was alone with Paddy. "He'll cream me!"

"Don't worry, kid. I've seen Gus wrestle. He's not as tough as he looks."

Rose thought for a moment. "Maybe you're right. Maybe I can beat him."

"Atta girl, Rose," said Paddy. "Just stick with me. We'll train like never before!"

Mountain Rose trained every single day for hours and hours. She ate only things that were good for her: spinach salad, Brussels sprouts, bran cereal, even liver and lots of juices. She refused chili-dogs, double-scoop ice-cream cones and chocolate-covered marshmallows.

Every day she followed the Flanagan Floor Plan: eighty sit-ups, forty push-ups, twenty chin-ups. Then she skipped rope for twenty minutes, jogged fourteen times around the gym and bicycled four miles. She lifted heavier and heavier weights.

By the day of the match she was going to be ready. Really ready.

NINE

Gus had his own training program. He slept late, watched soap operas and stuffed his face.

On Monday, Gus went to Arnie's Pit and had five orders of barbecued spareribs, four baked potatoes with sour cream and chives, and three hot fudge sundaes with whipped cream.

On Tuesday, he went to Lenny's Diner, where he devoured five stacks of pancakes drenched in butter and syrup, and washed it all down with three double chocolate milk shakes.

Wednesday, at Sol's Flickin' Chicken Place, Gus ate forty-three fried chicken wings, twelve orders of French fries with ketchup, and waffles and ice cream for dessert.

Thursday, at Uncle Louie's Deli, he ate four corned beef on pumpernickel, five pastrami on rye with Russian dressing and coleslaw, plus six pieces of Aunt Faye's Famous Cherry Cheesecake.

On Friday, Gus ordered a light snack—four hamburgers with onions, mustard, ketchup, relish, tomatoes and pickles, five orders of French fries and six Cokes. For dessert, he had only two Twinkies.

By the day of the match, Gus had gained twenty-five pounds and could hardly make it twice around the track.

TEN

The arena was packed. Gardenia Gus posters were everywhere. The crowd seemed to favour him.

"Lllladies and gennntlemen," shouted the ring announcer. "Now for the main event . . . the Wrestling Championship of the World. In this corner, in blushing pink, the Ladies' Champion . . . MOUNTAIN ROSE!"

The crowd started to boo and hiss.

"And in this corner, in basic black-ish acrylic trunks, the Men's Champion . . . GARDENIA GUS!"

The crowd went crazy. "Tear her to shreds!"

Mountain Rose and Gardenia Gus walked to the centre of the ring.

"Now I want a good, clean match," said the referee. "When the bell rings, come out fighting. And good luck."

Mountain Rose rushed back to her corner. "Gardenia Gus is gonna cream me. Please, coach—get me out of this!"

"Calm down, kid," said Paddy, massaging Rose's neck. "The guy's a slob. He's all blubber. Just kiss your lucky birthmark and get in there and fight. I'm with ya all the way."

Eleven

The bell rang. Rose and Gardenia Gus circled each other. Then Gus leaped in the air yelling: "BANZAI!" and tried a flying dropkick. Rose ducked. The crowd moaned. Gus jumped up, roared, and ran towards Rose. She tripped him, picked him up, and threw him down in a mighty body slam.

Gus was stunned. He shook his head. "Just warmin' up, folks," he kidded. "Gotta give the kid a chance." He wriggled out of Rose's hold.

But, like a flash, Rose had him in a headlock. The crowd cheered: "Show 'em, Rose. Hold him."

Gus shook free and started toward his corner.

"Come back here," shouted Rose, and she chased him across the ring. She reached out for Gus's trunks and grabbed. Gus kept running but his trunks didn't. The elastic stretched—and stretched—until his trunks slipped down.

And then Mountain Rose saw it.

On Gus's behind was a birthmark in the shape of an elephant on roller skates. A birthmark EXACTLY like the one on her wrist.

TWELVE

"Gus!" she cried and threw her arms around him. He grabbed his trunks and tried to get away. "I've found you—my long lost brother! I have the same birthmark on my wrist!"

"Rose? Is it YOU? The kid sister I've been looking for all my life?" Gus hugged her.

"What's going on here?" shouted the referee. "A wrestling championship or 'The Dating Game'?"

Rose explained. "Gus is my long-lost brother. When we were really little, we lived with our parents, who belonged to a circus. We were separated when our parents, The Flying Flushmans, missed the net. I was sent to live with Aunt Sadie, and Gus was sent to live with Aunt Sarah."

"Aunt Sarah and her dog both got asthma," Gus went on excitedly, "and we moved to the desert. Then Rose and Aunt Sadie moved and we lost touch. I thought I'd never see you again. You know, you're not a bad fighter, sis."

"Not a bad fighter?" Rose shouted. "I was WINNING this fight."

The referee lifted Rose's arm high into the air. "The winner is Mountain Rose, Champion Wrestler of the World."

The crowd was delighted. Gus looked embarrassed. Finally he smiled and put his arm around Rose. "Okay, okay," he shouted. "Ladies and gentlemen, Mountain Rose IS the best. Best wrestler, best sister."

Gus pulled Rose close. They hugged.

The crowd cheered, because even more than a good fight, people like a happy ending.

from

CHOCOLATE FEVER

by Robert Kimmel Smith

D irt breeds germs, Nurse Molly Farthing would often say, and germs have a nasty way of making healthy people ill. Naturally, the infirmary of P.S. 123 was always spotless because Nurse Molly Farthing wouldn't have it any other way. And naturally, as Mrs. Kimmelfarber and Henry rushed through the door that morning, she made both of them go back and wipe their feet on the mat. "And don't bring any of your cocoa in here," Nurse Farthing added. She sniffed the air loudly.

"Cocoa?" said Mrs. Kimmelfarber.

"Don't think I don't smell it," Nurse Farthing said.

"Please, Nurse Farthing," said Mrs. Kimmelfarber, "we have an emergency on our hands. This is Henry Green. He's breaking out in a rash of some sort."

"So I see," said Nurse Farthing. She sat Henry down in a chair and turned on a bright light. Pushing her spectacles down to the tip of her nose, she bent close to Henry and looked him over. "It's a rash all right," she said at last. "Peculiar. Looks like little brown spots all over."

"Exactly," Mrs. Kimmelfarber said. "But what is it?"

"Have you ever had measles?" Nurse Farthing asked.

"Yes," said Henry, "when I was five."

"Chicken pox?"

"When I was three and a half."

"Then I would say you have an unidentified rash. And frankly, I don't like the look of it."

Henry, who up until now was merely frightened, began to feel terrified. Nurse Farthing laid her cool hand on his arm and steadied him. "There, there, dear," she said. "Nothing to be frightened of. I'm sure it's not serious. How do you feel?"

"Not very good," said Henry.

"Warm?"

"No."

"Cold?"

"No."

"Dizzy?"

"No," said Henry. "I just feel . . . strange."

"You poor dear," said Nurse Molly Farthing, "you really must be frightened." She ran her fingers through his hair and patted the back of Henry's neck. Somehow this made him feel a little better.

Pop!

"Did you say something?" asked Nurse Farthing.

"No, ma'am," said Henry.

Pop!

"What is that noise, then?" she asked. "It sounds like something going pop."

"I heard it, too," said Henry.

"So did I," said Mrs. Kimmelfarber.

Pop! Pop! Pop! Now they all heard it. The sound of popping filled the infirmary. Little pops and bigger pops and poppity-pop-pops kept popping. Henry looked at his arm and in an instant knew where the noise was coming from. His little brown spots were growing bigger and bigger. They were popping out all over him. No longer the size of freckles, they were as big as the chocolate bits his mother used for making cakes and cookies. He could feel them popping out on his arms and face, could feel them growing under his shirt. In less time than it takes to tell it, Henry Green was covered with little brown lumps from the top of his head to the tip of his toes.

In later years, Henry couldn't remember who screamed first. All he could recall was that both he and Mrs. Kimmelfarber were yelling their heads off. And that Nurse Molly Farthing was as cool as a cantaloup.

"Calm down now, both of you," she said. "Mrs. Kimmelfarber, you go and call Mrs. Green on the telephone. Tell her we're taking Henry to the City Hospital."

Mrs. Kimmelfarber didn't move. She just stood there with her mouth open, staring at Henry.

"You scoot now," insisted Nurse Farthing in a stern tone. "Shoosh . . . off with you!

"And you, Henry Green," she said as Mrs. Kimmelfarber left the room, "are coming with me. Let us go. Quietly, Calmly."

She took his hand, and once again, Henry noticed that it felt good and somehow made him feel better. He kept holding her cool hand as they left the school. All the way to the hospital, as the taxi sped along, Henry held fast to the calm steady hand of Nurse Molly Farthing. In fact, it wasn't until he had been checked by two different doctors and was waiting to be examined by the hospital's chief of children's medicine, Dr. Fargo, that he dared to let go.

"What—what? What—what?" said Dr. Fargo as he came bounding into the examining room. He was a small, round man with a bushy white mustache and a confused look on his face. "What have we here, eh?" he asked. "Boy looks like he fell in a mud puddle."

He leaned down so close to Henry's nose that Henry could smell his puffy breath. It smelled like peppermints. "Didn't fall in a mud puddle, did you, lad?"

"No, sir."

"Didn't think so," said Dr. Fargo. "Too bad, would have explained what those big brown spots are all over you."

"Well, then," he said, turning to Nurse Molly Farthing, "tell me things."

"You're not going to believe this, Doctor," Nurse Farthing began, as she told Dr. Fargo about the events of the morning.

"I am not going to believe this," Dr. Fargo repeated when she had finished. "It's impossible. No rash in the whole history of rashes ever appeared so fast. Or grew so big. Or popped out with a noise you could hear. Impossible!"

"It happened," said Nurse Farthing.

"So I see. Well, we'll soon get to the bottom of this or my name's not . . . er. What is my name, by the way?"

"Dr. Fargo, I believe," said Henry.

"Pleased to meet you, son," said Dr. Fargo, and he shook Henry's hand. "Ought to do something about those big brown spots, though."

"Yes, sir," said Henry, who was beginning to feel confused himself.

Dr. Fargo took Henry to the examining table and switched on the big lamp. For a full five minutes he said nothing but "hmmmm" and "hah" as he poked and prodded Henry. He looked at every big brown spot and at all the bare spots in between the brown spots. He looked with a magnifying glass. In Henry's eyes and ears and nose and even under his tongue. Finally he said "I don't know any more than when I started. They look just like your typical big brown spots . . . except, of course, in the whole history of the civilized world there has never been a case of big brown spots before."

"I'm frightened," said Henry.

"I'm Dr. Fargo," said the doctor, "that much I know. Now what

I'd like to do is get to know more about those brown spots of yours."
He wet the tip of a cotton swab and brushed it gently against one
of the big brown spots on Henry's right arm.

"Ouch," said Henry.

"Did that hurt?"

"No."

"Then why did you say 'ouch'?"

"Because," said Henry, "I *thought* it was going to hurt."

"I see," said Dr. Fargo. Shaking his head, he put the cotton swab
into a glass jar. "Take this to the laboratory at once," he said to one
of his assistants, and the man rushed out of the room.

"In a few minutes we'll know more about those big brown spots
of yours," the doctor said. Hands behind his back, he began to pace
the room. Suddenly he stopped, his nose in the air. "Who has been
eating a candy bar in my office?" he demanded.

No one answered.

Dr. Fargo's nose twitched from side to side as he sniffed the air.

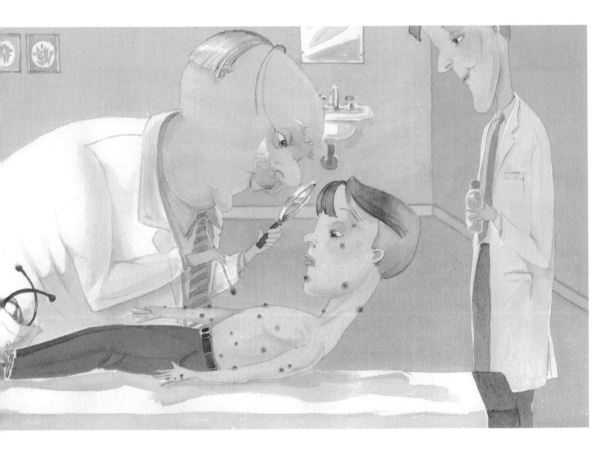

"I smell candy," he said. "Someone's been eating a candy bar."

Just then the telephone rang, and Dr. Fargo bounded across the room to answer it. "What—what?" he said into the phone. "Are you sure?" His moustache bounced up and down as Dr. Fargo sank slowly into a chair. He put the telephone down, a look of amazement on his face. "Chocolate," he said. "Those big brown spots . . . are pure chocolate. . . . "

"Chocolate?" gasped Nurse Farthing.

"Chocolate?" exclaimed Henry Green.

"Chocolate?" echoed Dr. Fargo's two assistants.

"Exactly," said Dr. Fargo. "The boy, it seems, is nothing more than a walking candy bar!"

GOOD PACKIN'

What I want to know is,
Is it good packin'?"
    You know what I mean.

The weather report tells me:
    temperature
    wind speed
    high pressure
    low pressure
    and how much snow.

    Did you hear that?
    "How MUCH snow!"
    Who cares!

"How MUCH snow!"
What I want to know is,
"What KIND?
Is it good packin'?"
    You know what I mean.

    Heavy to lift on the snow shovel, but
      snow forts,
      snowmen, and
      snowballs . . . BEAUTIFUL snowballs.
      You know what I mean.

Poems by Jack Booth

WORMSQUIRM

I know where the worms come from,
And I don't care what you say.
I found proof in my back yard,
In that big storm last Tuesday.

Take a look on dry, bright days,
And you won't find an earthworm.
Don't you see, it must be wet,
For you to see the WORMSQUIRM!

Worms just laugh at all the books,
And at both ends, they giggle.
They just wait for falling rain,
And then they start to wiggle.

I believe in my own proof,
But I won't say the books lie.
I just know where worms come from,
They come down from the RAIN SKY!

CHICOUTIMI

There once was a ghost from Chicoutimi,
Who used to sneak up and say boutimi.
One Hallowe'en night,
I gave him a fright,
Said the ghost, "Being scared is sure noutimi."

AWAY FROM HOME

by Peter Mayle

Staying the night at a friend's house is one of life's little pleasures. Parents are usually on their best behaviour. Bedtime is later than usual, and bathtime is often forgotten altogether. All in all, it's like a short holiday.

But because it's away from home, you must be prepared for everything to be different. For instance:

NOISES AT NIGHT

All houses have their own special set of night-time noises. You get so used to the sounds in your own house that you don't even notice them. But the minute you turn out the light in a strange room, you start hearing things. Crocodiles in the water pipes! Burglars under the bed! Giant toads outside the window! Snakes! Wolves! Help!

Put the light on, and they go away. Keep the light on, and they stay away.

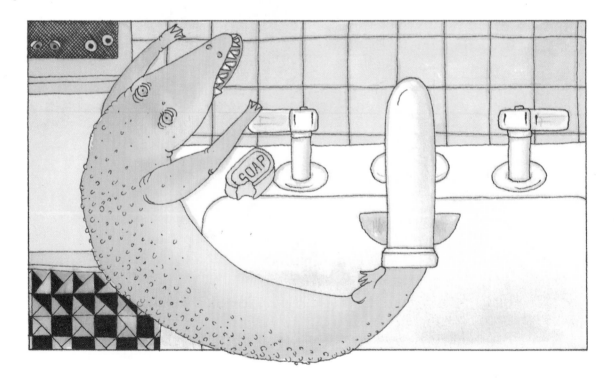

The Vanishing Loo

You know the way to the bathroom at home with your eyes closed, which is just as well when you need to go in the middle of the night. But where exactly is the bathroom in your friend's house? Could you find it in the dark? Are you sure? Goodness knows where you might end up if you're not certain of your geography.

Other People's Pets

One young friend of ours had a nasty shock when she was bitten by what she thought was a black rug. She stepped on it, and it turned into a dog. There are other stories of people being attacked by parrots they thought were stuffed, cats they thought were asleep, and hedgehogs that were supposed to be hibernating. The moral of these stories is: don't touch other people's pets unless you've been properly introduced.

Other People's Parents

They will always give you the benefit of the doubt the first time you do something awful. After that, they'll simply send you home. So you should treat them more carefully than your own parents until you get to know their little ways.

The Terrors of the Table

There are thousands of things you can eat. There are hundreds of ways of cooking them. But there are only three kinds of food.

1. Food that you like.
2. Food you're not sure about.
3. Food that makes you feel sick.

The first kind is the food you eat at home, and on birthdays. No difficulties there.

The second kind can give you some nasty moments. Not because of the food itself, but because it's always given to you when you're away from home. This can make even the most friendly plate of baked beans on toast look different and slightly suspicious.

When you're not sure about what's being dished up, it's best to ask for a small helping. You can't leave a huge plateful untouched and hope nobody will notice. But a small helping can be divided into even smaller blobs and left around the plate until it looks as though you've eaten most of it. If, to your surprise, you find that you actually like it, you can ask for more. Cooks are always pleased if you like their cooking.

It's the third kind of food that causes the most trouble. For us, it was always tapioca pudding (the stuff that looks like frogspawn), liver with tubes in it, or salad, which we were sure was infested with slugs. For you, it could be anything from macaroni cheese to pork chops. There are bound to be one or two things which make your heart sink as you see them coming towards you on the plate. You know that one mouthful—even without swallowing—will make you sick.

You can either sit there and drink umpteen glasses of water while the Thing on your plate gets cold and even more disgusting. Or you can do this: just say, "I'm very sorry, but liver (or whatever it is) doesn't agree with me."

This is a pleasant and polite way of saying no. Any sensible person will leave it at that, and not ask you to force down a couple of mouthfuls. People who do insist have only themselves to blame for what happens next.

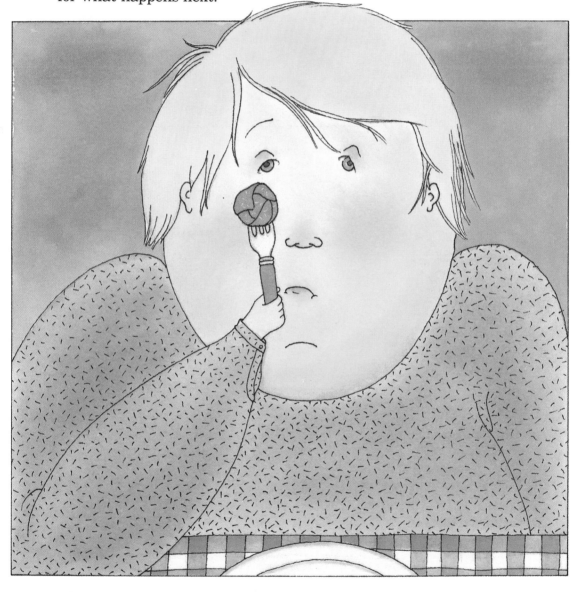

GREEN

by Joe Raposo

It's not that easy bein' green,
Having to spend each day the colour of the leaves,
When I think it could be nicer bein' red, or yellow, or gold,
Or something much more colourful like that.

It's not easy bein' green,
It seems you blend in with so many other ordinary things,
And people tend to pass you over, 'cause you're not standing out
Like flashy sparkles on the water or stars in the sky.

But green is the colour of spring,
And green can be cool and friendly like,
And green can be big like an ocean
Or important like a mountain or tall like a tree.

When green is all there is to be,
It could make you wonder why,
But why wonder, why wonder?

I am green and it'll do fine,
It's beautiful and I think it's what I want to be.

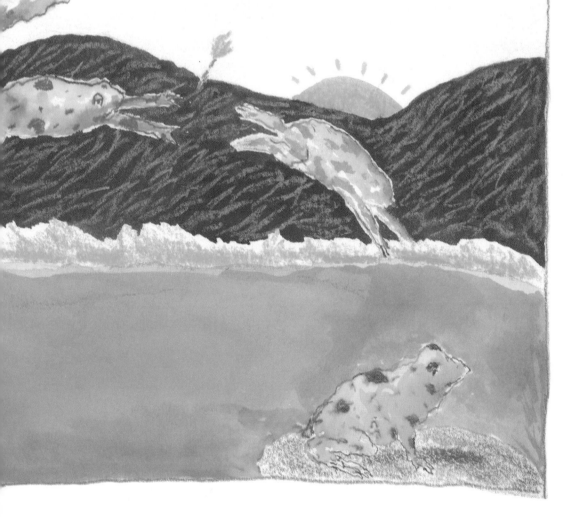

THE STRANGE STORY OF THE FROG WHO BECAME A PRINCE

by Elinor Lander Horwitz

Many years ago there was a handsome frog who lived by a rather nice pond.

He had fun all day and at night he had happy dreams. Every day was exactly the same as every other day.

He liked to swim in the pond and hop in the grass. He hopped high and he hopped low. When he was feeling silly he hopped sideways.

In the grass and in the pond the handsome frog found caterpillars, grasshoppers, and many other good things to eat.

His skin was green like the grass and brown like the pond and gold like the sun. He had black eyes which poked out on either side of his head.

He was a very handsome frog indeed.

One day he was minding his own business, catching caterpillars and doing some rather fine hopping when a wicked witch came swimming across the pond. She had a wet black hat and a wet black dress and she had black eyes right on the front of her face. She looked like a bad dream.

But the handsome frog thought she looked rather interesting.

"Will you join me for a lunch of caterpillar?" he asked the wicked witch as he took a happy sideways jump. "I'd be happy to cut mine in half."

"ICK!" said the wicked witch, making a face.

"What did you say?" he asked.

"People don't eat caterpillars," she said, making a face. "ICK!"

The frog looked at the interesting witch who had a face like a bad dream. "What do people eat if they don't eat caterpillars?" he asked.

The witch put her hand into her big wet pocket and took out a very soggy peanut butter sandwich.

"Have some of this," she said. "I'll share it with you. It's delicious." She broke the sandwich in half and handed him a piece.

The frog bit into the sandwich. "ICK!" he said.

The wicked witch looked at the handsome frog. She smiled a wicked smile. Then she snapped her fingers and said

ECNIRP!

which sounded like a hiccup but which is really PRINCE spelled backwards.

Instantly the handsome frog turned into a prince.

"What have you done to me?" he asked.

"I've changed you into a prince," she said. "Aren't I clever?"

"But why?" he asked.

"Because I wanted to," she said.

He looked at his pink skin and felt his big ears and the hair on his round head. "My skin is as smooth as a worm, and my ears are like leaves, and my head has grass growing on it!" he cried. "Please change me back into the handsome frog I used to be."

The wicked witch smiled. "Oh, I can't do that," she said. "I don't remember how."

"Why, oh why did you do such a careless thing?" the prince asked, weeping. "I was such a handsome happy frog and then along you came and turned me into an ugly prince."

The wicked witch said, "I wanted to see if I could still do magic. Many years ago I changed a handsome prince into an ugly frog.

What a good trick *that* was! But he was unhappy too. People are so unadventurous. Did you ever hear of him?"

"Indeed I did," said the prince. "They say he cried all day and frightened the polliwogs with all that talk about witches. They say he was a very low hopper and a slow swimmer as well. When he disappeared everyone said he had been changed back into a prince. Now, how did you do *that*?"

The witch shrugged. "Who can remember? It was years and years ago."

"Try to remember," said the prince.

"It was all part of a magic spell I've forgotten"

The prince said, "What was that magic word you said when you changed me into a prince?"

"I said PRINCE backwards," she said. "Some magic spells work that way. You have to keep trying new words because some work and some don't, although I've never known why."

"Well, try saying that one again," said the prince.

ECNIRP!

said the witch loudly.

Nothing happened.

"Try FROG backwards," said the prince.

"GORF!" said the witch.

"Try WATER."

"RETAW!"

"Try SUN."

"NUS!"

"Try GRASS."

"SSARG," she hissed.

The prince thought hard and then said softly, "Try MAGIC WORD."

"What a good idea, said the witch. "CIGAM DROW!!!"

Nothing happened.

The prince sat down in the tall grass and began to cry again, more loudly than before.

"Now, stop that," said the witch. "I don't know if you know this, but ANYONE WOULD RATHER BE A PRINCE THAN A FROG."

"Really?" asked the prince. "Why?"

The witch thought hard for a moment and then she said, "Well, for one thing, you can have a name when you're a person. A name tells people who you are. Pick any name you like and it will be yours. How about a fine name like TOM?"

"TOM?" said the prince. "Is that a name? It sounds like something falling in the grass at night when it's dark."

"How about HARRY?" asked the witch.

"Is *that* a name?" asked the prince. "It sounds like a cricket calling."

"What about a noble, princely French name like ALPHONSE?" asked the witch.

"It sounds like a beaver sneezing," said the prince.

"You really are a difficult person to please," said the witch. "Look at your nice clothes. Clothes keep you warm and make you look nice."

"Warm!" said the prince. "My legs are strangling. I'm boiling. I can hardly jump."

"Only necks can strangle," said the witch. "Only water can boil. Only frogs and horses and grasshoppers jump around in that boring way. And furthermore," said the witch, "people can learn how to read." She took a wet newspaper out of her wet pocket.

"You see, these are words," she said. "Look, this word says 'pond'."

"Pond?" he said. "It doesn't look like a pond at all. It looks just like muddy hummingbird footprints."

"How old are you anyhow?" said the witch.

"I was born in the spring," said the frog.

"Well, no wonder," said the witch. "You can't learn to read until you're six years old. I'm very sorry, but I don't know how to break the spell," said the witch, a little crabby now. "You'll just have to learn to like being a prince. Come now, I'll teach you how to whistle and snap your fingers. Now *there* are two things no frog can do."

The witch whistled "Row, Row, Row Your Boat" for the prince.

The prince tried and tried, but he could not whistle.

"Why would anyone want to whistle or snap his fingers anyhow?" asked the prince.

"Whistling is a very useful trick," said the witch. "You can call your dog when you whistle."

"I hate dogs," said the prince.

"Well, never mind," said the witch. "I'll teach you how to snap your fingers."

The witch snapped her fingers.

And suddenly she remembered.

She remembered that she had not snapped her fingers when she said her magic words backwards.

She leaned closer to the poor unhappy prince, looked into his sad eyes, snapped her fingers, and said:

CIGAM DROW!

"I feel different!" said the prince.

"Why, look what I've done!" said the witch. "I've changed you into a beautiful princess! How charming!"

"HOW EMBARRASSING!!" said the princess who used to be a prince who used to be a frog. "Keep trying, please. I think you're on the right track."

SSARG!

said the witch, snapping her fingers.

And the princess who used to be a prince who used to be a frog changed again.

"You're getting warmer," said the centaur who used to be a princess who used to be a prince who used to be a frog.

The witch snapped her fingers again and said:

NUS! RETAW!

The merman who used to be a centaur who used to be a princess who used to be a prince who used to be a frog said, "Almost, but not quite. Try again."

The witch snapped her fingers very loudly twice and cried:

GORF! GORF!

And the spell was broken.

The handsome frog was very happy. He looked at himself in the pond, and he hopped high and he hopped low. Then he hopped sideways. He swam across the pond and back. He ate a caterpillar.

"If you change your mind and want to be a prince again, just call me," said the witch, as she put on her swimming goggles.

"Oh, no!" said the frog. "But if I meet someone else who would like to be changed into a prince, how do I find you?"

"Just whistle or snap your fingers, and I'll be there," said the witch, as she jumped into the pond and swam away.

The handsome frog laughed. He laughed and laughed until he was very tired. Then he sat down on a warm rock and told the whole story to a tree toad, who didn't believe it.

RECESS

TANGLE TALK

I went to the pictures tomorrow
And took a front seat at the back
I fell from the pit to the gallery
And broke a front bone in my back
The lady she gave me some chocolate
I ate it and gave it her back
I phoned for a taxi and walked it
And that's why I never came back.

If the butterfly courted the bee,
    And the owl the porcupine;
If the churches were built in the sea,
    And three times one was nine;
If the pony rode his master,
    If the buttercups ate the cows,
If the cat had the dire disaster
    To be worried, sir, by the mouse;
If mamma, sir, sold the baby,
    To a gypsy for half a crown;
If a gentleman, sir, was a lady—
    The world would be Upside-down!
If any of all these wonders
    Should ever come about,
I should not consider them blunders,
    For I should be Inside-out!

I dreamed a dream next Tuesday week,
    Beneath the apple tree;
I thought my eyes were big pork-pies,
    And my nose was Stilton cheese.
The clock struck twenty minutes to six,
    When a frog sat on my knee;
I asked him to lend me a dollar bill,
    But he borrowed a quarter off me.

On Christmas Eve I turned the spit,
I burnt my fingers, I feel it yet,
The cock sparrow flew over the table;
The pot began to play with the ladle.
The ladle stood up like an angry man,
And vowed he'd fight the frying-pan;
The frying-pan behind the door
Said he never saw the like before—
And the kitchen clock I was going to wind
Said he never saw the like behind.

We're all in the dumps,
    For diamonds are trumps;
The kittens are gone to St. Paul's!
    The babies are bit,
    The moon's in a fit,
And the houses are built without walls.

THE MIDDLE OF
THE WEB

Everyone likes a good mystery. We enjoy the shivers that run up and down our spine when we are in the middle of a scary story, or when we are watching a "who-done-it" film. We try to solve the problem before the detective does, or we imagine what is going to happen to the hero or the heroine.

In this excerpt, a strange thing has happened on the farm, and a mystery is about to begin.

"This is a very serious thing, Edith," he replied. "Our pig is completely out of the ordinary."

"What's unusual about the pig?" asked Mrs. Zuckerman, who was beginning to recover from her scare.

"Well, I don't really know yet," said Mr. Zuckerman. "But we have received a sign, Edith—a mysterious sign. A miracle has happened on this farm. There is a large spider's web in the doorway of the barn cellar, right over the pigeon, and when Lurvy went to feed the pig this morning, he noticed the web because it

was foggy, and you know how a spider's web looks very distinct in a fog. And right spang in the middle of the web there were the words 'Some Pig.' The words were woven right into the web. They were actually part of the web. I know, because I have been down there and seen them. It says 'Some Pig,' just as clear as can be. There can be no mistake about it. A miracle has happened and a sign has occurred here on earth, right on our farm, and we have no ordinary pig."

"Well," said Mrs. Zuckerman, "it seems to me you're a little off. It seems to me we have no ordinary spider."

(from *Charlotte's Web*, by E.B. White)

A strange message sent in the night. What a perfect way to begin a story that will pull you inside and make you part of the mystery. All of the selections in this section are connected with mysterious places, strange people, and even a spooky evening called Hallowe'en. Welcome to the middle of the mystery web!

THE CASE OF
THE MYSTERIOUS TRAMP

by Donald J. Sobol

His head bent low over the handlebars of his bike, Encyclopedia Brown rounded the corner of Maple Avenue like high-speed sandpaper.

It was three minutes before six o'clock of a summer evening. With a bit of luck and a following wind, Encyclopedia hoped to make it home on time for dinner.

Suddenly someone called his name.

"Leroy! Leroy Brown!"

Right off he knew it had to be a teacher calling. Only teachers and his mother and father called him Leroy.

Everyone else in the town of Idaville called him Encyclopedia.

He didn't look much like an encyclopedia, which is a set of books filled with all kinds of facts. Or even like one book.

People called him Encyclopedia because he had read more books than a bathtub full of professors. And he never forgot anything he read.

"Leroy! Leroy!"

It was Mrs. Worth, his old fourth-grade teacher. She was standing beside her car looking very sad.

"I can't get it going," she said. "Can you help me?"

"I'll try," said Encyclopedia. He leaned his bike against a tree and raised the hood.

"Start her again, please, Mrs. Worth," he said.

The motor coughed and sputtered out.

"The trouble must be in the carburetor," said Encyclopedia, beginning to disappear behind the hood.

He lifted off the air filter. Now he could reach the butterfly valve in the carburetor. He poked it open with his finger.

The motor roared to life when Mrs. Worth again tried to start it.

Mrs. Worth was delighted. When Encyclopedia returned to view,

she thanked him over and over again.

"Golly, it wasn't anything," said Encyclopedia. "Just a stuck valve."

He smiled as Mrs. Worth drove off—till he looked at his watch. It gave him unsmiling news. It was past six o'clock, the Brown's dinner hour. He'd catch it for being late!

His mother put down a pot of boiled cabbage to stare at him. Dirt and grease from Mrs. Worth's motor coated him from ears to sneakers.

"Where have you been?" she asked, kissing the one clean spot on his cheek.

"Fishing," answered Encyclopedia.

"In an oil well?"

"The water was so dirty," Encyclopedia said quickly, "the gold-fish looked like black bass."

He didn't mention Mrs. Worth's motor. He seldom spoke to any-one, not even his parents, about the help he gave others. And he *never* spoke about the help he gave grown-ups.

His mother looked out at Rover Avenue through the kitchen window. Oddly, she hadn't scolded him for being late.

"Your father knows we are having corned beef and cabbage tonight," she said in a worried voice. "What could be keeping him?"

"Dad wouldn't miss his favourite dish without a good reason," said Encyclopedia. "Maybe he's chasing a dangerous crook or something."

Mrs. Brown looked even more worried.

Encyclopedia tried again. "Don't worry, Mom," he said. "Dad is the best police officer in the state. He'll be home soon."

Encyclopedia was right. As he was washing the back of his neck, he heard his father close the garage door.

A moment later Mr. Brown entered the house. He was a big broad-shouldered man dressed in a police chief's uniform.

His uniform was the envy of every lawman in the United States. Although Idaville was like many other American towns, its police force was *un*like any other.

For more than a year, neither child nor grown-up had got away with breaking a law.

Hardened criminals had passed the word: "Stay clear of Idaville."

This was partly because the Idaville policemen were well trained, smart, and brave. But mostly it was because Chief Brown had Encyclopedia at the dinner table.

Chief Brown never whispered a word of how Encyclopedia helped him. After all, who would believe the truth?

Who would believe that a fifth-grader solved difficult cases while eating dinner in the Brown's red brick house on Rover Avenue?

Naturally, Encyclopedia never let out that he was the mastermind behind Idaville's war on crime.

So the name Leroy Brown was missing from the honour roll of the world's greatest detectives.

"I'm sorry to be late, dear," said Chief Brown as he sat down to eat. "A terrible thing happened this afternoon."

After he had said grace, he raised his head and looked at

Encyclopedia. "Mr. Clancy, the plumber, was beaten and robbed."

"Was he badly hurt?" asked Mrs. Brown.

"He's in St. Mark's Hospital," Chief Brown said. "The doctors say he'll be all right. I'm afraid we'll never catch the man who attacked him."

"Why not, Dad?" asked Encyclopedia. "Didn't anyone see what happened?"

"John Morgan saw everything," said Chief Brown. "He's Mr. Clancy's helper. He was sitting in the truck when a tramp attacked Mr. Clancy."

Chief Brown unbuttoned his breast pocket and drew out his notebook. "I wrote down everything John Morgan told me. I'll read it to you."

Encyclopedia closed his eyes. He always closed his eyes when he did his heavy thinking on a case.

His father began to read what John Morgan had told him about the beating and theft.

"Mr. Clancy was driving the truck and I was sitting beside him. We had turned onto the dirt road near the Benson farm when the motor overheated. Clancy stopped, walked around to the front of the truck, and lifted the hood. As he took off the radiator cap, a tramp jumped out of the woods. The tramp struck Clancy on the head with a piece of pipe.

"Clancy fell over the radiator and slid down the front of the truck. I leaped out of the truck, but the tramp was already racing into the woods. He carried the pipe and Clancy's wallet. I let him go in order to get Clancy to the hospital right away."

Chief Brown finished reading and closed his notebook.

Encyclopedia opened his eyes. He asked but one question: "Did Mr. Clancy have an unusually large amount of money in his wallet?"

His father looked startled.

"Why, yes," he answered. "It so happened that Mr. Clancy had two hundred dollars in his wallet. He had just been paid for work on a new apartment house. What made you think he was carrying a lot of money?"

"He had to be," said Encyclopedia. "Now you should have no trouble finding the man who struck and robbed him."

"No trouble?" said Chief Brown. "The woods come out on the railroad tracks. It's a sure bet that the tramp hopped a ride on a freight train. He's probably in Georgia by now."

"You'll find him where John Morgan lives—and the two hundred dollars besides," said Encyclopedia.

"Do you think John Morgan helped the tramp rob Mr. Clancy?" asked Mrs. Brown.

"No," answered Encyclopedia.

"Well, what do you think?" asked Chief Brown.

"I think that when Mr. Clancy stopped the truck in the woods, John Morgan saw his chance," answered Encyclopedia. "While Mr. Clancy was checking the radiator, John Morgan sneaked from the truck, knocked him out, and stole his wallet with the two hundred dollars."

"What about the tramp?" asked Chief Brown.

"There never was a tramp, Dad," said Encyclopedia. "John Morgan made him up. John Morgan robbed Mr. Clancy by himself and then drove him to the hospital."

Chief Brown rubbed his chin thoughtfully. "That could be what really happened," he said. "But I can't prove it."

"The proof is down in black and white," said Encyclopedia. "Just read over what John Morgan told you. He gives himself away!"

HOW DID JOHN MORGAN GIVE HIMSELF AWAY

?

John Morgan said that Mr. Clancy walked around to the front of the truck and raised the hood.

He described how "Clancy fell over the radiator and slid down the front of the truck" after being struck by the tramp. Then he himself "climbed out of the truck."

But he said he had been sitting in the front seat. So he saw the attack through the windshield.

Impossible! The hood of the truck was raised, remember?

All John Morgan could have seen through the windshield was the hood!

Chief Brown recovered Mr. Clancy's money. The guilty John Morgan was sent to prison.

RETURN TO AIR

by Philippa Pearce

The Ponds are very big, so that at one end, people bathe and at the other end they fish. Old chaps with bald heads sit on folding stools and fish with rods and lines. But the water's much deeper at our end of the Ponds, and that's where we bathe. You're not allowed to bathe there unless you can swim; but I've always been able to swim. They used to say that was because fat floats—well, I don't mind. They call me Sausage.

Only, I don't dive—not from any diving board, thank you. I have to take my glasses off to go into the water, and I can't see without them, and I'm just not going to dive, even from the lowest diving board, and that's that, and they stopped nagging about it long ago.

Then, this summer, they were all on me to learn duck-diving. You're swimming on the surface of the water and suddenly you go up-end yourself just like a duck and dive down deep into the water, and perhaps you swim around a bit underwater, and then come up again. I daresay ducks begin doing it soon after they're born. It's different for them.

So I was learning to duck-dive—to swim down to the bottom of the Ponds, and pick up a brick they'd thrown in, and bring it up again. You practise that in case you have to rescue anyone from drowning—say, they'd sunk for the third time and gone to the bottom. Of course, they'd be bigger and heavier than a brick, but I suppose you have to begin with bricks and work up gradually to people.

The swimming instructor said, "Sausage, I'm going to throw the brick in—" It was a brick with a bit of old white cloth round it, to make it show up underwater. "—Sausage, I'm going to throw it in, and you go *after* it—go *after* it, Sausage, and get it before it reaches the bottom and settles in the mud, or you'll never get it."

He'd made everyone come out of the water to give me a chance, and they were standing watching. I could see them blurred along

the bank, and I could hear them talking and laughing: but there wasn't a sound in the water except me just treading water gently, waiting. And then I saw the brick go over my head as the instructor threw it, and there was a splash as it went into the water ahead of me; and I thought: I can't do it—my legs won't up-end this time— they feel just flabby—they'll float, but they won't up-end—they *can't* up-end—it's different for ducks. . . . But while I was thinking all that, I'd taken a deep breath, and then my head really went down and my legs went up into the air—I could feel them there, just air around them, and then there was water round them, because I was going down into the water after all. Right down into the water . . . straight down.

At first my eyes were shut, although I didn't know I'd shut them. When I did realize, I forced my eyelids up against the water to see. Because, although I can't see without my glasses, as I've said, I don't believe anyone could see much underwater in those Ponds; so I could see as much as anyone.

The water was like a thick greeny-brown lemonade, with wispy little things moving very slowly about in it—or perhaps they were just movements of the water, not things at all; I couldn't tell. The brick had a few seconds' start on me, of course, but I could still see a whitish glimmer that must be the cloth round it: it was ahead of me, fading away into the lower water, as I moved after it.

The funny thing about swimming underwater is its being so still and quiet and shady down there, after all the sunlight and splashing and shouting just up above. I was shut right in by the quiet, greeny-brown water, just me alone with the brick ahead of me, both of us heading towards the bottom.

The Ponds are deep, but I knew they weren't too deep; and, of course, I knew I'd enough air in my lungs from the breath I'd taken. I knew all that.

Down we went, and the lemonade-look quite went from the water, and it became just a dark blackish-brown, and you'd wonder you could see anything at all. Especially as the bit of white cloth seemed to have come off the brick by the time it reached the bottom

and I'd caught up with it. The brick looked different down there, anyway, and it had already settled right into the mud—there was only one corner left sticking up. I dug into the mud with my fingers and got hold of the thing, and then I didn't think of anything except getting up again with it into the air.

Touching the bottom like that had stirred up the mud, so that I began going up through a thick cloud of it. I let myself go up—they say fat floats, you know—but I was shooting myself upwards, too. I was in a hurry.

The funny thing was, I only began to be afraid when I was going back. I suddenly thought: perhaps I've swum underwater much too far—perhaps I'll come up at the far end of the Ponds among all the fishermen and foul their lines and perhaps get a fishhook caught in my cheek. And all the time I was going up quite quickly, and the water was changing from brown-black to green-brown and then to bright lemonade. I could almost see the sun shining through the water, I was so near the surface. It wasn't until then that I felt really frightened: I thought I was moving much too slowly and I'd never reach the air again in time.

Never the air again. . . .

Then suddenly I was at the surface—I'd exploded back from the water into the air. For a while I couldn't think of anything, and I couldn't do anything except let out the old breath I'd been holding and take a couple of fresh, quick ones, and tread water—and hang on to that brick.

Pond water was trickling down inside my nose and into my mouth, which I hate. But there was air all round and above, for me to breath, to live.

And then I noticed they were shouting from the bank. They were cheering and shouting, "Sausage! Sausage!" and the instructor was hallooing with his hands round his mouth, and bellowing to me: "What on earth have you got there, Sausage?"

So then I turned myself properly round—I'd come up almost facing the fishermen at the other end of the Pond, but otherwise only a metre from where I'd gone down; so that was all right. I turned round and swam to the bank and they hauled me out and gave me my glasses to have a good look at what I'd brought up from the bottom.

Because it wasn't a brick. It was just about the size and shape of one, but it was a tin—an old, old tin box with no paint left on it and all brown-black slime from the bottom of the Ponds. It was as heavy as a brick because it was full of mud. Don't get excited, as we did: there was nothing there but mud. We strained all the mud through our fingers, but there wasn't anything else there—not even a bit of old sandwich or the remains of bait. I thought there might have been, because the tin could have belonged to one of the old chaps that have always fished at the other end of the Ponds. They often bring their dinners with them in bags or tins, and they have tins for bait, too. It could have been dropped into the water at their end of the Ponds and got moved to our end with the movement of the water. Otherwise, I don't know how that tin box can have got there. Anyway, it must have been there for years and years, by the look of it. When you think, it might have stayed there for years and years longer; perhaps sunk underwater forever.

I've cleaned the tin up and I keep it on the mantelpiece at home with my coin collection in it. I had to duck-dive later for another brick, and I got it all right, without being frightened at all; but it didn't seem to matter as much as coming up with the tin. I shall keep the tin as long as I live, and I might easily live to be a hundred.

WELCOME

Poems by sean o huigin

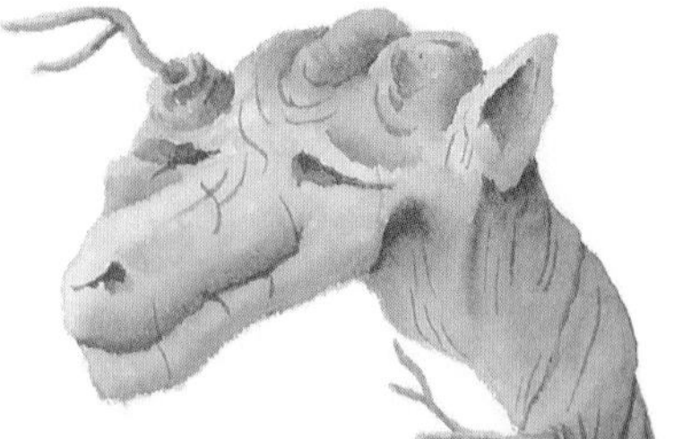

this is a poem
for those who
are brave
it starts at
the mouth of
a very old
cave
a goblin will
greet you
as you walk
in
his hair long
and greasy
and his green teeth
agrin
his eyes red
and tiny
his face
grey and mean
he'll grab
at your hand
and let out
a scream

he'll lead you
down tunnels
much darker
than night
he'll take
you past
monsters that
will try to
bite
the toes off
your footsies
the ears off
your head
you soon
will start
wishing
you'd stayed
home in bed
worms wet
and slimy
will crawl
up your back

and as you
go further
it really
gets black
you can't see
a thing
and all you
can hear
is a creaky old
voice
that says
"come my dear
let's see if
you're chunky
let's feel
if you're fat
i'm hungry
today
NO
STOP
DON'T GO BACK"
but if you are
clever
you'll get
out of there
or you'll end
in some stomach
no one knows where

THE POCKET

i reached
into my
pocket
and much
to my surprise
something in
there
grabbed me
and pulled
me right
inside
i felt
its clammy
fingers
all bony
cold and
thin

i tried to
keep my
head out
no use
it all went in
and that
was not
the end
of it
the pocket
seemed
so deep
and dark
and strange
and scary
i felt i
had to
weep

"shut up
you silly
creature"
a voice
yelled
in my
ear
and then
my feet
were
pulled inside
and i had
disappeared

How to Get Rid of
Bad Dreams

by Nancy Hazbry

If you dream you are being chased down a lonely
road by a bunch of ugly monsters with pointy
horns and jagged teeth and terrible claws,
don't worry.

All you have to do is . . .

take a mirror out of your pocket and hold it in
front of them. When the monsters see
themselves, they will be so scared they'll turn
around and run the other way.

If you dream you are walking in the park
on a sunny afternoon when a huge dragon jumps
out at you from behind a bush and tries to fry you
with his fiery breath, don't worry.

All you have to do is . . .

pull your shrink-ray laser
out of your belt and fire until the
dragon shrivels to the size of a kitten.
Then you can be the only one in school with
your own pet dragon.

If you dream you get lost in a jungle and step
into quicksand up to your waist, and every move
just makes you sink deeper and deeper, don't worry.

All you have to do is . . .

take off your hat and have a sip
from the bottle of reducing potion in your
knapsack. Soon you will be small enough to fit
in your hat and you can row to safety.

If you dream you are being attacked by
one-hundred-and-ninety-nine billion black, scary,
hairy bugs with green eyes and red stingers, don't worry.

All you have to do is . . .

whip out a can of silver paint and spray it all
over the bugs, then take a deep breath and blow
them into the sky. That will make one-hundred-
and-ninety-nine billion new glittering stars.

If you dream you are just sitting down to lunch
after climbing the highest mountain in the world,
and suddenly a fierce wind starts to blow you
right over the edge into a bottomless crevice,
and you have dropped your pick,
and your rope is getting frayed,
don't worry.

    All you have to do is . . .

chew six pieces of really sticky bubble
gum, stick a great wad on the bottom
of each foot and walk back down
the mountain.

If you dream that

a scary ghost uttering horrible moans and groans,
a bunch of ugly monsters with pointy horns and jagged teeth and
    terrible claws,
a huge dragon with fiery breath,
one-hundred-and-ninety-nine billion scary, hairy bugs with green
    eyes and red stingers,
and a warty, bristly troll
are chasing you, and you are stuck
in bottomless quicksand in the jungle,
in a fierce wind at the top of the highest mountain in the world,
or in the dark inside of a giant's nose
and if you can't figure out what to do, don't worry.

    All you have to do is . . .
                  is . . .
                     is . . .
                        is . . .

THE TAILYPO

by Joanna Galdone

A long time ago an old man lived by himself in the deep, big woods. His cabin had only one room, and that room was his parlour, his bedroom, his dining room and his kitchen, too.

The old man had three dogs. One was called Uno, one was called Ino, and one was called Cumptico-Calico.

One day the man decided to go hunting to catch something for his supper. "Here, here, here!" he shouted to his dogs, and they came bounding off the porch, eager for a chase.

After many hours of hunting, the wind began to blow hard from the valley. "It'll be dark soon," the old man said, "and all we've caught is this skinny rabbit." He headed home, afraid he might go to bed hungry that night.

The old man cooked and ate the rabbit and gave the bones to

the dogs. Then he leaned back in his chair and watched the moon as it rose up big and full. The wind whistled around the cabin.

Just as the old man was about to doze off, a most curious creature crept through a crack between the logs in the wall. It had a BIG, LONG, FURRY TAIL.

As soon as the old man saw the varmint he reached for his hatchet, and with one lick he cut its tail off! Before the man could raise his hatchet a second time, the creature slipped out through the crack and ran away.

The old man was still hungry, so he took that big, long tail, cooked it, and ate it. After that, he stuffed up the crack in the wall and went to bed.

His stomach was full and he felt so warm and snug that before he knew it he was asleep. The old man hadn't been asleep very long when he woke up. Something was climbing up the side of his cabin. It sounded like a cat,

SCRATCH,

SCRATCH,

SCRATCH.

"Who's that?" the old man asked. He lay still and listened, and after a while he heard a voice say:

*"Tailypo, tailypo,
all I want is my tailypo."*

The scratching went on and on, and the old man began to shiver and shake. Then he remembered his dogs. He went to the door and called, "Here, here, here!"

The dogs came piling out from under the porch, and with their noses to the ground they chased that thing into the deep, big woods. The old man pulled his covers tightly around him and went back to sleep.

In the middle of the night he woke up again. Now he heard something trying to get in right above the cabin door.

"Who's that?" he called. "And what do you want at this time of night when all good folks should be in bed?" He listened and he could hear it going, SCRATCH, SCRATCH, SCRATCH. Then he heard the voice say:

*"Tailypo, tailypo,
I'm coming to get my tailypo!"*

The old man was so scared he couldn't stand up. So he called his dogs from his bed, "Uno, Ino, Cumptico-Calico. Here, here, here!" And those dogs came bursting around the corner of the cabin. They caught up with that wild thing at the gate and tore the whole fence down trying to get at it. Then they chased it into the swamp.

At last all was quiet again. With a weary sigh, the man went back to sleep. Toward morning something down in the swamp woke up the old man. First he thought it was the wind blowing louder than usual. But when he listened again, he heard that voice crying:

*"You know and I know,
all I want is my tailypo."*

The old man called his dogs, "Here, here, here! Uno, Ino, Cump-tico-Calico!" This time the dogs didn't come.

The old man ran outside into the moonlight and called again, "Here, dogs, here, here, here!" But there was no trace of them. There was just the sound of the wind blowing around the torn-down fence. That thing had led the dogs way off into the swamp and lost them.

Sadly the man went back inside the cabin and shut and barred the door. Then he went back to bed. Just before daylight the old man opened his eyes, the way people do when they feel there's some-one else in the room. Something was stirring among the pots and pans. Then something that sounded just like a cat began climbing up the covers at the foot of the bed. The man listened and heard it, SCRATCH, SCRATCH, SCRATCH.

He looked over the foot of his bed and saw two pointed ears. Then he saw two big, round fiery eyes staring at him. The man wanted to call for help, but he was too scared. That thing kept on creeping up until it was right next to the old man. Then it said in a low voice:

> "*You know and I know,*
> *that I'm here to get my tailypo.*"

The man sat up and pulled the covers over his head. All at once he got his voice and said, "I haven't got your tailypo!"

"Yes, you have," said the thing, "Yes, you have." And it jumped on top of that man and scratched everything to pieces.

Now there's nothing left of the old man's cabin in the deep, big woods except the chimney. But folks who live in the valley say that when the moon shines and the wind blows, you can hear a voice say:

> "*Tailypo, tailypo,*
> *now I've got my tailypo.*"

from

THE BFG

by Roald Dahl

S ophie couldn't sleep.

A brilliant moonbeam was slanting through a gap in the curtains. It was shining right onto her pillow.

The other children in the dormitory had been asleep for hours.

Sophie closed her eyes and lay quite still. She tried very hard to doze off.

It was no good. The moonbeam was like a silver blade slicing through the room onto her face.

The house was absolutely silent. No voices came up from downstairs. There were no footsteps on the floor above either.

The window behind the curtain was wide open, but nobody was walking on the pavement outside. No cars went by on the street. Not the tiniest sound could be heard anywhere. Sophie had never known such silence.

Perhaps, she told herself, this was what they called the witching hour.

The witching hour, somebody had once whispered to her, was a special moment in the middle of the night when every child and every grown-up was in a deep, deep, sleep, and all the dark things came out from hiding and had the world to themselves.

The moonbeam was brighter than ever on Sophie's pillow. She

decided to get out of bed and close the gap in the curtains.

You got punished if you were caught out of bed after lights-out. Even if you said you had to go to the lavatory, that was not accepted as an excuse and they punished you just the same. But there was no one about now, Sophie was sure of that.

She reached out for her glasses that lay on the chair beside her bed. They had steel rims and very thick lenses, and she could hardly see a thing without them. She put them on, then she slipped out of bed and tip-toed over to the window.

When she reached the curtains, Sophie hesitated. She longed to duck underneath them and lean out of the window to see what the world looked like now that the witching hour was at hand.

She listened again. Everywhere it was deathly still.

The longing to look out became so strong she couldn't resist it. Quickly, she ducked under the curtains and leaned out of the window.

In the silvery moonlight, the village street she knew so well seemed completely different. The houses looked bent and crooked, like houses in a fairy tale. Everything was pale and ghostly and milky-white.

Across the road, she could see Mrs. Rance's shop, where you bought buttons and wool and bits of elastic. It didn't look real. There was something dim and misty about that too.

Sophie allowed her eye to travel further and further down the street.

Suddenly she froze. *There was something coming up the street on the opposite side.*

It was something black . . .

Something tall and black . . .

Something very tall and very black and very thin.

WHO?

It wasn't a human. It couldn't be. It was four times as tall as the tallest human. It was so tall its head was higher than the upstairs windows of the houses. Sophie opened her mouth to scream, but no

sound came out. Her throat, like her whole body, was frozen with fright.

This was the witching hour all right.

The tall black figure was coming her way. It was keeping very close to the houses across the street, hiding in the shadowy places where there was no moonlight.

On and on it came, nearer and nearer. But it was moving in spurts. It would stop, then it would move on, then it would stop again.

But what on earth was it doing?

Ah-ha! Sophie could see now what it was up to. It was stopping in front of each house. It would stop and peer into the upstairs window of each house in the street. It actually had to bend down to peer into the upstairs windows. That's how tall it was.

It would stop and peer in. Then it would slide on to the next house and stop again, and peer in, and so on all along the street.

It was much closer now and Sophie could see it more clearly.

Looking at it carefully, she decided it *had* to be some kind of PERSON. Obviously it was not a human. But it was definitely a PERSON.

A GIANT PERSON, perhaps.

Sophie stared hard across the misty moonlit street. The Giant (if that was what he was) was wearing a long BLACK CLOAK.

In one hand he was holding what looked like a VERY LONG, THIN TRUMPET.

In the other hand, he held a LARGE SUITCASE.

The Giant had stopped now right in front of Mr. and Mrs. Goochey's house. The Goocheys had a greengrocer's shop in the middle of High Street, and the family lived above the shop. The Goochey children slept in the upstairs front room, Sophie knew that.

The Giant was peering through the window into the room where Michael and Jane Goochey were sleeping. From across the street, Sophie watched and held her breath.

She saw the Giant step back a pace and put the suitcase down on the pavement. He bent over and opened the suitcase. He took something out of it. It looked like a glass jar, one of those square ones with a screw top. He unscrewed the top of the jar and poured what was in it into the end of the long trumpet thing.

Sophie watched, trembling.

She saw the Giant straighten up again and she saw him poke the trumpet in through the open upstairs window of the room where the Goochey children were sleeping. She saw the Giant take a deep breath and *whoof*, he blew through the trumpet.

No noise came out, but it was obvious to Sophie that whatever had been in the jar had now been blown through the trumpet into the Goochey children's bedroom.

What could it be?

As the Giant withdrew the trumpet from the window and bent down to pick up the suitcase he happened to turn his head and glance across the street.

In the moonlight, Sophie caught a glimpse of an enormous long pale wrinkly face with the most enormous ears. The nose was as sharp as a knife, and above the nose there were two bright flashing eyes, and the eyes were staring straight at Sophie. There was a fierce and devilish look about them.

Sophie gave a yelp and pulled back from the window. She flew across the dormitory and jumped into her bed and hid under the blanket.

And there she crouched, still as a mouse, and tingling all over.

THE SNATCH

Under the blanket, Sophie waited.

After a minute or so, she lifted a corner of the blanket and peeped out.

For the second time that night her blood froze to ice and she wanted to scream, but no sound came out. There at the window, with the curtains pushed aside, was the enormous long pale wrinkly face of the Giant Person, staring in. The flashing black eyes were fixed on Sophie's bed.

The next moment, a huge hand with pale fingers came snaking

in through the window. This was followed by an arm, an arm as thick as a tree-trunk, and the arm, the hand, the fingers were reaching out across the room towards Sophie's bed.

This time Sophie really did scream, but only for a second because very quickly the huge hand clamped down over her blanket and the scream was smothered by bedclothes.

Sophie, crouching underneath the blanket, felt strong fingers grasping hold of her, and then she was lifted up from her bed, blanket and all, and whisked out of the window.

If you can think of anything more terrifying than that happening to you in the middle of the night, then let's hear about it.

The awful thing was that Sophie knew exactly what was going on although she couldn't see it happening. She knew that a Monster (or Giant) with an enormous long pale wrinkly face and dangerous eyes had plucked her from her bed in the middle of the witching hour and was now carrying her out through the window smothered in a blanket.

What actually happened next was this. When the Giant had got Sophie outside, he arranged the blanket so that he could grasp all the four corners of it at once in one of his huge hands, with Sophie imprisoned inside. In the other hand he seized the suitcase and the long trumpet thing and off he ran.

Sophie, by squirming around inside the blanket, managed to push the top of her head out through a little gap just below the Giant's hand. She stared around her.

She saw the village houses rushing by on both sides. The Giant was sprinting down High Street. He was running so fast his black cloak was streaming out behind him like the wings of a bird. Each stride he took was as long as a tennis court. Out of the village he ran, and soon they were racing across the moonlit fields. The hedges dividing the fields were no problem to the Giant. He simply strode over them. A wide river appeared in his path. He crossed it in one flying stride.

Sophie crouched in the blanket, peering out. She was being bumped against the Giant's leg like a sack of potatoes. Over the fields and hedges and rivers they went, and after a while a frightening thought came into Sophie's head. *The Giant is running fast,* she told herself, *because he is hungry and he wants to get home as quickly as possible, and then he'll have me for breakfast.*

THE CAVE

The Giant ran on and on. But now a curious change took place in his way of running. He seemed suddenly to go into a higher gear. Faster and faster he went and soon he was travelling at such a speed that the landscape became blurred. The wind stung Sophie's cheeks. It made her eyes water. It whipped her head back and whistled in her ears. She could no longer feel the Giant's feet touching the ground. She had a weird sensation they were flying. It was impossible to tell whether they were over land or sea. This Giant had some sort of magic in his legs. The wind rushing against Sophie's face became so strong that she had to duck down again into the blanket to prevent her head from being blown away.

Was it really possible that they were crossing oceans? It certainly felt that way to Sophie. She crouched in the blanket and listened to the howling of the wind. It went on for what seemed like hours.

Then all at once the wind stopped its howling. The pace began to slow down. Sophie could feel the Giant's feet pounding once again over the earth. She poked her head up out of the blanket to have a look. They were in a country of thick forests and rushing rivers. The Giant had definitely slowed down and was now running more normally, although normal was a silly word to use to describe a galloping giant. He leaped over a dozen rivers. He went rattling through a great forest, then down into a valley and up over a range of hills as bare as concrete, and soon he was galloping over a desolate wasteland that was not quite of this earth. The ground was flat and pale yellow. Great lumps of blue rock were scattered around, and dead trees stood everywhere like skeletons. The moon had long since disappeared and now the dawn was breaking.

Sophie, still peering out from the blanket, saw suddenly ahead of her a great craggy mountain. The mountain was dark blue and all around it the sky was gushing and glistening with light. Bits of pale gold were flying among delicate frosty-white flakes of cloud, and over to one side the rim of the morning sun was coming up red as blood.

Right beneath the mountain, the Giant stopped. He was puffing mightily. His great chest was heaving in and out. He paused to catch his breath.

Directly in front of them, lying against the side of the mountain, Sophie could see a massive round stone. It was as big as a house. The Giant reached out and rolled the stone to one side as easily as if it had been a football, and now, where the stone had been, there appeared a vast black hole. The hole was so large the Giant didn't even have to duck his head as he went in. He strode into the black hole still carrying Sophie in one hand, the trumpet and the suitcase in the other.

As soon as he was inside, he stopped and turned and rolled the great stone back into place so that the entrance to his secret cave was completely hidden from outside.

Now that the entrance had been sealed up, there was not a glint of light inside the cave. All was black.

Sophie felt herself being lowered to the ground. Then the Giant let the blanket go completely. His footsteps moved away. Sophie sat there in the dark, shivering with fear.

He is getting ready to eat me, she told herself. He will probably eat me raw, just as I am.

Or perhaps he will boil me first.

Or he will have me fried. He will drop me like a rasher of bacon into some gigantic frying-pan sizzling with fat.

A blaze of light suddenly lit up the whole place. Sophie blinked and stared.

She saw an enormous cavern with a high rocky roof.

The walls on either side were lined with shelves, and on the shelves there stood row upon row of glass jars. There were jars everywhere. They were piled up in the corners. They filled every nook and cranny of the cave.

In the middle of the floor there was a table twelve feet high and a chair to match.

The Giant took off his black cloak and hung it against the wall. Sophie saw that under the cloak he was wearing a sort of collarless shirt and a dirty old leather waistcoat that didn't seem to have any buttons. His trousers were faded green and were far too short in the legs. On his bare feet he was wearing a pair of ridiculous sandals that for some reason had holes cut along each side, with a large hole at the end where his toes stuck out. Sophie, crouching on the floor of the cave in her nightie, gazed back at him through thick steel-rimmed glasses. She was trembling like a leaf in the wind, and a finger of ice was running up and down the length of her spine.

"Ha!" shouted the Giant, walking forward and rubbing his hands together. "What has us got here?" His booming voice rolled around the walls of the cave like a burst of thunder.

The Giant picked up the trembling Sophie with one hand and carried her across the cave and put her on the table.

Now he really is going to eat me, Sophie thought.

Now the Giant sat down and stared hard at Sophie. He had truly enormous ears. Each one was as big as the wheel of a truck and he seemed to be able to move them inwards and outwards from his head as he wished.

"I is hungry!" the Giant boomed. He grinned, showing massive square teeth. The teeth were very white and very square and they sat in his mouth like huge slices of white bread.

"P . . . please don't eat me," Sophie stammered.

"*Me!*" shouted the Giant, his mighty voice making the glass jars rattle on their shelves. "Me gobbling up human beans! This I never! The others, yes! All the others is gobbling them up every night, but not me! I is a freaky Giant! I is a nice and jumbly Giant! I is the only nice and jumbly Giant in Giant country! I is the Big Friendly Giant! I is the BFG. What is *your* name?"

"My name is Sophie," Sophie said, hardly daring to believe the good news she had just heard.

THE WITCH

by Jack Prelutsky

She comes by night, in fearsome flight,
in garments black as pitch,
the queen of doom upon her broom,
the wild and wicked witch,

a cackling crone with brittle bones
and desiccated limbs,
two evil eyes with warts and sties
and bags about the rims,

a dangling nose, ten twisted toes
and folds of shrivelled skin,
cracked and chipped and crackled lips
that frame a toothless grin.

She hurtles by, she sweeps the sky
and hurls a piercing screech.
As she swoops past, a spell is cast
on all her curses reach.

Take care to hide when the wild witch rides
to shriek her evil spell.
What she may do with a word or two
is much too grim to tell.

BUNYA THE WITCH

by Robert Kraus

Once upon a time, there was a very tiny old lady and her name was Bunya. Tiny Bunya lived alone in a very old tumble-down cottage on the outskirts of a small village. Every day all the children of the village came to Bunya's to tease and torment her.

> *"Bunya, Bunya,*
> *You're a witch!*
> *Bunya, Bunya,*
> *Dig a ditch!"*

chanted all the children.

> *"Sticks and stones*
> *will break my bones*
> *but names will never hurt me,"*

Bunya chanted back.

So the children threw sticks and stones as well as mud at her.

"Witch! Witch!" they cried as they threw.

"I'm not a witch!" cried Bunya. "I'm *not*! I'm *not*!"

"Okay, Bunya," said a loud boy. "If you're not a witch, prove it!"

"That's right," said his friend. "If you're not a witch, prove it!"

"Prove it! Prove it! Prove it!" screamed all the children.

"Prove that I'm not a witch?" said Bunya. "Who can prove they're not a witch? If I *was* a witch, *that* I could prove. I would make a motion and say, 'Hocus Pocus!'"

Immediately there was a loud clap of thunder and a crashing bolt of lightning and all the children were turned into frogs!

"I am a witch," groaned Bunya. "I *am* a witch!" And Bunya the witch collapsed in a heap, sobbing, moaning, wringing her hands, cracking her knuckles and pounding the earth.

In the village square the great clock knelled the hour of six. Bong, bong, bong, bong, bong, bong. It was supper time. But instead of hungry children—frogs!

"A plague of locusts I've heard of," said an old man, "a plague of frogs is a first."

Frogs! Frogs! Frogs! Everywhere frogs! All the mothers and fathers were throwing frogs out of their houses as the frogs tried to sit down and eat their children's dinner. (They little realized that the frogs *were* their children!) No sooner was a frog thrown out, than quick as a wink he jumped back in, only to be thrown out again.

Then the mayor of the village, who was a scholar and very wise man, looked into the eyes of the frog who was trying to eat his son's supper. "This frog is our son!" he cried. "Our beloved Emile!"

So saying, he kissed his frog son and his eyes filled with tears—as did the eyes of his frog son Emile.

"Let me kiss Emile too," said the mayor's wife. "After all, I am this frog's mother!"

"Kiss, kiss," said the mayor, sobbing.

Suddenly he tapped his head. "Aha!" he said. "I've got it!" "Witchcraft!" he cried. "Courtesy of Bunya the witch."

So saying, the mayor clutched his frog son to his heart and with his wailing wife behind him, ran into the streets crying, "Bunya the witch has changed my darling son Emile into a frog!"

"She's changed my sweet daughter Sophie," sobbed the butcher. "A sweeter girl you couldn't find. Now she's a frog!"

"Bunya's changed my twin darlings into twin frogs!" cried the baker.

And all the villagers ran out of their houses crying and clutching their frog children. They gathered in the village square. There was crying and wailing and gnashing of teeth and sad croaking from the frog children.

Then the mayor tapped his forehead again. "I've got an idea," he said, drying his tears and blowing his nose. "Bunya the witch changed our children into frogs, Bunya the witch can change our frogs back into children."

"Why didn't I think of that?" said the butcher.

"Because you're not as smart as I am," said the mayor.

"Don't argue," said the baker. "On to Bunya's!"

"On to Bunya's! On to Bunya's!" chanted the villagers.

So with the mayor leading the way, all the mothers and fathers marched to Bunya's tumble-down cottage on the edge of the village. Bunya was still in a heap—sobbing, moaning, wringing her hands, cracking her knuckles and pounding the earth.

"Bunya, you terrible witch," said the mayor, "you have done a monstrous, horrible thing!"

"You're telling me," said Bunya. "I know, I know. But it's all a big mistake. I was trying to prove to your children that I wasn't a witch. I made a motion. I said 'Hocus Pocus' . . . "

Immediately there was a loud thunderclap and a crashing bolt of lightning and all the mothers and fathers turned into pigs!

"I've done it again!" groaned Bunya. Poor Bunya was shaking so much, she went into the house to make a glass of hot tea with lemon to calm her nerves.

"First frogs by mistake. Now pigs by mistake," groaned Bunya, as she sipped her hot tea with lemon.

"Croak, croak," croaked the frogs.

"Oink, oink," oinked the pigs.

"Such a racket," sighed Bunya. "Who needs all this trouble? Not me. After all these years, suddenly I'm a witch! Such a thing to discover at my age. Magic powers. Phfui! Who needs them? But also who needs all these frogs and pigs?"

Then Bunya got an idea!

Bunya made a motion and said "Pocus Hocus!" Immediately there was a loud thunderclap and a big bolt of lightning and all the frogs and pigs turned back into children and mothers and fathers!

The mothers and fathers were all very frightened now that they knew from experience that Bunya was a witch. They were also very respectful. They inquired after her health and bowed and scraped, trying not to displease Bunya in any way, so that Bunya would not cast any more spells on them.

"Dear Bunya, I hope you are enjoying your old age," said the mayor.

"What's to enjoy?" replied Bunya.

"I'll send you a fresh chicken already plucked, sweet Bunya," said the butcher.

"I'll send you some fresh day-old bread, kindly Bunya," said the baker.

"Has anyone ever told you you are a good-looking old lady?" said the wine merchant.

"Bunya, Bunya,
You're a peach!
Bunya, Bunya,
Make a speech!"

chanted all the children.

Bunya raised her hands to silence them.

"Please, Bunya, no more Hocus Pocus!" pleaded the mayor, falling to his knees.

"Nobody's making Hocus Pocus!" said Bunya. "I'm holding up my hands for silence. Now listen to me. I didn't need your insults. I don't need your compliments. Do me a favour, will you please?"

"Anything, anything you say, pretty Bunya," said the villagers.

"Stop calling me pretty Bunya and go home and mind your own

business and let me mind mine, which happens to be being a witch."

"Whatever you say, good, sweet Bunya," replied the villagers, and they left walking backwards.

At last Bunya was alone. "So if I'm a witch, I'm a witch. Magic powers aren't the worst thing in the world to have. Maybe I could use them to help the poor, and who is poorer than poor Bunya? Nobody! There is one thing I have *always* wanted to do—travel. Now, in my old age, thanks to my magic powers, I can."

So Bunya the witch got on her broomstick and sailed away into the sky to see the world.

from
THE WITCH WHO WASN'T
by Jane Yolen

Isabel was a witch!

At least she should have been a witch.

Her mother was a witch. Her mother's mother was a witch. In fact, all her relatives back as far as she could remember had been witches, which, if you are a witch, is very far indeed.

She had a black cat. And bats in her belfry. A long, twiggy broom. And a very tall broad-brimmed, pointed-top, brass-buckled, very black hat.

Yes, Isabel was a witch!

At least she should have been a witch. Her mother . . . oh, yes, you already know that. But Isabel wasn't. She was a witch who wasn't!

You see, she didn't look like a witch. Her eyes twinkled a merry blue. Her hair turned up at the ends. And so did the brim of her hat. And her cat—well, it was really more of a kitten.

Isabel's spells? They were of no more use than the charms on a charm bracelet. She just could not make anything evil.

Isabel could turn a bat into a cat, a snake into a chocolate cake, and a bug into something huggable. In fact, when she stirred the family cauldron, it would begin to smell ever so faintly of sugar and spice. But not one evil thing at all.

On her last birthday, Isabel was seven hundred years old, but she looks only seven. That's because it takes witches so much longer to grow up. They grow a year older every hundred years.

When a witch is seven hundred years old, she is allowed to go to the Witches' Convention. That's a special Hallowe'en party where witches from all over the world gather once a year. It starts at midnight and continues until the first rays of light creep over the distant hills. Then each witch jumps on her own broom and rides home. The sky before dawn is filled with flying witches, shooting like fast black skyrockets north, south, east, and west.

Every young witch looks forward to Hallowe'en and the Witches' Convention. Every young witch is excited about trying her witching in the Spelling Bee.

But Isabel wasn't.

She was a witch who wasn't.

"I know they will just laugh at me," Isabel said sadly to Nuncle, her cat. Nuncle was lying half asleep on the bed. "They will tease me about my hair and my eyes. They will laugh at my hat and my spells. But, worst of all, they will call you a pretty kitty. Imagine, a witch with a pretty kitty. And, oh, Nuncle, it's true."

Nuncle purred. Then he stirred, twitching his whiskers and crinkling his long silky-black tail.

"Oh," Isabel sighed, "I wish I wasn't a witch."

But wishing, even for witches, solves nothing.

Just then her mother called out, "Isabel. It's time for your chores."

Her chores! At seven, when the sun was tucked firmly behind the mountains, Isabel got up. At eight she stirred the family cauldron. Then she vanished outside to practise her spells.

"Don't forget your mumbo jumbo," called her mother, as Isabel sadly walked through the wall.

Outside, by a dead tree, Isabel practised her spells. "One, two, one, two," she said. Her magic wand went up and down in time to the chant.

On the last word, Isabel pointed her wand at a spider spinning its way toward a fly. Fire flashed from the wand. The web burst in a puff of smoke. A frisky puppy fell out of the smoke and chased Nuncle up the tree.

"Oh, no," said Isabel. She sat down on the cold ground and began to cry. "It's just impossible. I'm not even a little bad. I'll never learn to spell correctly. And tonight is Hallowe'en. I'll disgrace Mother and Grandma. What shall I do?"

She looked up at Nuncle, who crouched, trembling, in the fork of the tree. "Come down, you silly kitten," she said tearfully. "It's only a witched dog. There's no need for you to run away.

"Run away! That's what I'll do, I'll run away!" Isabel looked around wildly for a direction in which to run.

But it was too late. Her mother was calling.

"Isabel, come in and dirty up. And be sure to forget to wash behind your ears. We have to get ready for the party."

"Party?" crackled Grandma. "Oh, yes, time for the party." She hobbled over to the magic mirror on the wall, and looked in. "Mirror, mirror on the wall, who's the ugliest witch of all?"

But the mirror said nothing. It had a crack in it.

"Oh, bother," said Grandma to herself. She turned to Isabel, who had just come into the house. "Are you ready to leave, my dear?"

Isabel smiled sadly. "I have to feed the bats and dust the floor first," she said. She got out the box of dust and began sprinkling the room with it.

"Don't forget to wax your wand well," Grandma whispered. "It might help you with the Spelling Bee."

"Oh, Grandma," said Isabel, as two tears started out of her eyes, "we all know I'll be the first witch in this family who wasn't a winner. The only witch who wasn't."

"It will come," said Isabel's mother, as she fluffed up the cobwebs near the door. "It just takes time and practice. Let's go!"

Grandma put on her dusty black hat. "Let's go," she said in her high voice.

"Let's go," Isabel repeated softly.

NEWFOUNDLAND RIDDLES

What's got
a tongue and
cannot talk?

Shoe

What is that
which belongs to you
But others use it more than you do?

Your Name

What goes over the water
and under the water
And never touches the water?

Egg inside a duck

Four legs up and four legs down,
Soft in the middle and hard all aroun'.

Bed

Riddle me, riddle me, what is that
Over the head and under the hat?

Hair

Round as a marble,
deep as a cup,
All the king's army
couldn't lift it up.

Well

What lives in winter,
dies in summer,
And grows with its roots upward?

Icicle

What goes up the hill
and down the hill,
And spite of all, yet standeth still?

Road

What's got an eye
and cannot see?

Needle

What goes 'round the house
and leaves but one track?

Wheelbarrow

'Round the house and 'round the house
And into the corner it goes.

Broom

A houseful, a roomful,
Couldn't catch a cupful.

Smoke

What has four legs
and smokes a pipe?

Stove

What drinks his own blood
and eats his own flesh?

Burning lamp

A row of white horses
upon a red hill,
Here they goes, here they goes,
here they stops still.

Teeth

I haven't got it
and I don't want it,
but if I had it,
I wouldn't sell it
for a thousand dollars.

Bald head

WHERE AM I?

Do you dream of make-believe places and fantasy worlds? When you read a good book, you often find yourself inside the story, as your imagination takes you on a journey. Writers of fantasy stories enjoy making up weird and amazing places where real-life people struggle against strange powers. Do you ever imagine what it would be like to find yourself in a fantasy world? Perhaps this excerpt—about characters who are so small that they can fit into a boot—will help you look at the world through different eyes.

Arriety was the first to wake. "Where am I?" she wondered. She felt warm—too warm, lying there between her mother and her father—and when she turned her head slightly she saw three little golden suns, floating in the darkness. It was a second or two before she realized what they were, and with this knowledge, memory flooded back—all that happened yesterday: the escape, the frenzied scramble across the orchard, the weary climb, the rain. The little golden suns, she realized, were the lace-holes of the boot!

She slid out from between her sleeping parents and just as

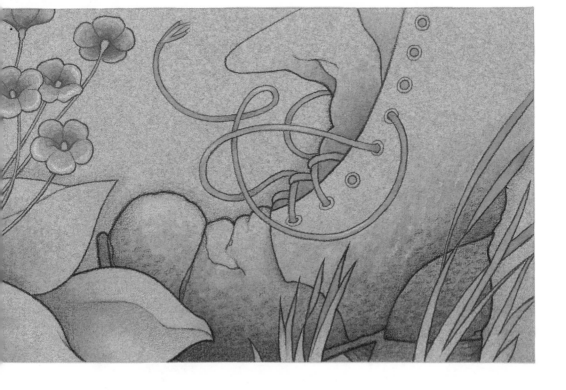

she was, in bare feet and in her vest and petticoat, she ventured out-of-doors.

It was a glorious day: sunlit and rain-washed—the earth breathing out its scents. "This," Arriety thought, "is what I have longed for; what I have imagined: what I knew existed—what I knew we'd have!"

She pushed through the grasses and soft drops of water fell on her benignly, warmed by the sun. There was warm mud here, between the shorter grass blades, fast-drying now in the sun. A bank rose between her and the hedge—a glorious bank, it was, filled with roots, with grasses, with tiny ferns, with small sandy holes, with violet leaves and with pale scarlet pimpernel, and, here and there, a globe of deeper crimson—wild strawberries!

(from *The Borrowers Afield*, by Mary Norton)

What dangers would you fear if suddenly you were only one-tenth your size? Can you picture yourself and your new viewpoint and ask "Where am I?" Then you are ready to meet the fantasy worlds in this section.

THE WITCH AND
THE RAINBOW CAT

by Terry Jones

A small girl was walking along the banks of a river on a hot
summer's day when, quite by chance, she came across a little
house. It had a front door and windows and a chimney and a little
garden that ran down to the river, but it was very, very small. The
girl could touch the roof if she reached up, and she had to bend her
head to look in at the windows.

"I wonder if anyone's at home?" she said to herself. So she knocked
on the door and waited, but there was no answer. So she tried the
door and it opened easily.

"Hello?" she called. "Is there anyone at home?" But there was
no answer. Now the little girl knew that she shouldn't go into a
strange house without being invited, but it was all so curious and
so small that she just *had* to look inside. So she bent her head, and
stepped into the house.

Everything in the house was perfect, but half the size of normal
things. She didn't have to stand on tip-toe to look on to the tables.

She didn't have to stand on a chair to reach the kitchen sink or look out of the windows, and the door handles were all just the right height. There was a sitting room with a fireplace and a mirror over the mantelpiece, and she could see into the mirror perfectly well, just like her mother could at home, without having to climb on anything. But she noticed one very curious thing: the reflection of herself that she saw in the mirror was quite grown up.

At first she thought it was a trick of the light, and she looked around the room at the other things, but when she turned back to the mirror, sure enough—instead of a little girl, there was a fully grown-up woman looking back at her. She blinked and stared again. It was definitely *her* reflection: the dress it was wearing was exactly the same as the dress she was wearing, and when she touched her nose the reflection touched *its* nose, and when she touched her ear, the reflection touched *its* ear . . . and suddenly she realized—she was looking at herself as a grown-up woman.

How long she stood there, staring into that mirror, I don't know, but suddenly she heard the latch on the front door open, and she heard some footsteps coming slowly into the house . . . tip . . . tap . . . tip . . . tap . . . and all at once she remembered that she shouldn't be there, so she quietly hid herself behind a little cupboard, feeling very frightened.

She heard the footsteps go into the kitchen . . . tip . . . tap . . . tip . . . tap . . . and then go out of the kitchen and slowly start to come towards the sitting room . . . tip . . . tap . . . tip . . . tap. Nearer and nearer they came and the little girl's heart beat faster and faster, until the footsteps stopped and turned and went upstairs. The little girl took her chance and ran for the front door, but it was locked. She ran to the back door, but that too was locked, and there was no key. She tried the windows but they were all tight shut, and she couldn't open any of them. And so she ran back and hid behind the cupboard in the sitting room.

Well, she crouched there for quite a long time, wondering what on earth she was going to do, when she heard the footsteps coming downstairs again . . . tip . . . tap . . . tip . . . tap. This time they turned towards the sitting room and kept on coming, closer and closer, until they walked right in. The little girl peered out from behind the cupboard, and do you know what she saw? She saw a little old witch in a green hat and a green cloak, and on her shoulder was a cat that was all the colours of the rainbow.

The little girl didn't know what to do, so she just kept quiet. And the little old witch stopped and looked about her, and said: "Who's been looking in my mirror? I can see a child there!"

The poor girl trembled with fright and kept just as quiet as she could, but she heard the little old witch coming towards the cupboard, and suddenly there she was, looking down at her with piercing green eyes.

"Who are you?" asked the old witch. "What are you doing in my house?"

"Please," said the little girl, "my name is Rose and I didn't mean any harm."

"*Didn't* mean any harm?" screamed the old witch. "Didn't mean any *harm*! You've looked in my mirror!"

"Please," said Rose, "shouldn't I have done?"

"Of course you shouldn't have!" screamed the witch. "Now I'll have to keep you here forever!"

"Oh please, let me go home," cried Rose, "and I'll never come and bother you again."

"No! You've looked in my mirror!" cried the witch. "You can't go back now! You'll stay here and be my servant!"

Well, poor Rose wept and pleaded with the little green witch, but there was nothing she could do. The witch took her up to the attic at the top of the little house and locked her in. The attic had no windows and was bare and dark and full of cobwebs. Poor Rose sat down on the dusty floor and cried, for she didn't know what she was going to do.

Suddenly she felt something soft brushing up against her, and she nearly jumped out of her skin. But when she looked down she found it was just the rainbow-coloured cat, rubbing itself up against her legs.

"Hello," said the rainbow cat. "You can ask me three questions."

Rose was so astonished to hear the cat talk that, without stopping to think, she exclaimed: "But how is it you can talk?"

The rainbow cat yawned and replied: "I would have thought that was obvious—the witch put a spell on me. Two questions left. If I were you, I'd think more carefully about the next."

Rose thought carefully about the next question, and then asked: "Why doesn't the witch like me looking in her mirror?"

"A better question," replied the cat, stretching itself. "She doesn't like you looking in the mirror because she is the Witch of the Future, and in that mirror she sees the things that are to come. She is the only person that can know those things, and once you know them she'll never let you go. One question left."

Rose thought very carefully about what was the best question to ask the rainbow cat next, but try as she might she could not decide. She thought: "If I ask him how to escape from here, that wouldn't stop the old witch catching me again. If I ask him how I can get home, that wouldn't stop the old witch from finding me there. . . . "

At length the rainbow cat asked: "Well? Have you thought of your last question?"

"Not yet," replied Rose.

"Very well," said the cat, "I'll wait."

Just then the door flew open and in burst the witch. She thrust a bundle of old clothes towards Rose and said: "Here is a servant's uniform. You must put it on, or I'll turn you into a mad dog."

Poor Rose trembled with fright but she took off her own clothes and put the uniform on. It was grey and drab, and it made her feel miserable.

"Now," said the witch, "you must work for me." And she made poor Rose scrub the floors from morning till evening, all that day and all the next day. And when Rose begged to be allowed to do some other work, the Witch of the Future shook her head and said: "No! You must keep your eyes on the floor so that you don't go looking in my mirror again."

Poor Rose had to scrub the witch's floors day in, day out, and at night she was so exhausted that she would go to bed without once raising her eyes from the floor. Day after day, week after week, the witch kept her at it, until poor Rose's back was bent and her hands were sore, and she never raised her eyes from the floor ever. And she worked so hard that she forgot about everything else until, one day, when the witch was out in the forest collecting toads, Rose suddenly felt the rainbow cat rubbing itself up against her leg.

"Rainbow cat! I'd forgotten about you!" she cried.

"Well," said the cat, "have you thought of your last question yet?"

Rose stopped her scrubbing for a moment, and then said: "I'll ask you my last question tomorrow."

"Very well," said the cat, "I'll wait."

All that night, although she was exhausted from her scrubbing, Rose couldn't sleep. She was too busy trying to work out the best question to ask the rainbow cat, but she still couldn't decide.

The next morning she could hardly get up to scrub the floors, and she kept yawning and feeling faint.

"Now then!" screamed the Witch of the Future. "What are you doing? Get on with your scrubbing, girl, or I'll turn you into a cabbage and make you into cabbage soup!"

Then the witch went out to the forest to catch some bats. Rose was scrubbing the doorstep, watching the witch go, when she noticed a small bird in the garden, with its leg caught in one of the witch's traps. Although Rose knew that the witch would be very angry, she couldn't bear to see the bird in such pain, and so she put down her scrubbing brush and went and released it, and then went back to her scrubbing.

The next moment, she felt something rub against her leg and there was the rainbow cat again.

"Well," said the rainbow cat, "have you thought of your last question?"

"Not quite," said Rose.

"I can't wait any longer," replied the rainbow cat.

Just then, the bird flew down and landed on Rose's shoulder, and said: "I can tell you what to ask." And it whispered in Rose's ear, and then flew off again.

"Well," said the rainbow cat, "what is your question?"

Rose looked at the cat and took a deep breath and then said as the bird had told her: "Tell me, rainbow cat, why can't I choose my own future?"

At these words the rainbow cat looked up and smiled, and his colours all started changing and glowing and spinning round and round. "But you can!" he cried: "The Witch of the Future has no power without her mirror—break that and you are free."

Just then, Rose looked up and saw the witch coming out of the woods towards her. Without another word, Rose turned and ran back into the little house, and took the mirror off the wall and hurled it to the ground so that it smashed into smithereens. Everything went still. Then there was a dreadful scream, and there glaring at her in the doorway stood the Witch of the Future, only she looked a thousand years older. Rose summoned up all her courage but, before she could speak, the witch stumbled and fell to the floor. At that moment Rose heard a creak, and saw the wall of the house start to crumble. So she ran, and she didn't stop running until she reached the gate at the bottom of the garden. There she turned, in time to see the little house collapse in a cloud of dust, and an ordinary black cat walked out and rubbed against her legs.

"Is that you, rainbow cat?" asked Rose. But the cat didn't reply. It simply strolled off into the woods. And Rose changed into her own clothes, and ran home as fast as she possibly could.

THE RAINBOW GOBLINS
by Ul de Rico

O nce there was a land that lived in fear of seven goblins. They were called the Rainbow Goblins and each had his own colour, which was also his name: Red, Orange, Yellow, Green, Blue, Indigo and Violet. Yellow, being the craftiest, was their chief. The goblins lived on colour—they prowled the valleys and climbed the highest mountains looking for rainbows, and when they found one, they caught it in their lassos, sucked the colours out of it and filled their bellies with its bright liquid.

Only one place in the land had never known goblin-fear—the hidden valley called the Valley of the Rainbow, where the great

arches of colour were born. There the animals still lived in paradise.

But the Rainbow Goblins had heard tales of this Valley, and their mouths watered whenever they thought of the feast that awaited them there; and so they gathered up their lassos and their pails and set off.

With great effort, the goblins made their way over the jagged piles of rock that guarded the entrance. When the climbing became difficult, Yellow roared: "Don't lose heart, comrades! Think of the delicious colours ahead!"

The sun had almost set by the time they reached their goal—the very meadow where the Rainbow sprang to life. Immediately beneath the meadow they found a cave. "We'll spend the night here," the Yellow Goblin commanded.

When the moon rose and saw them warming themselves around

the fire they had lit, it shouted out in alarm: "The Rainbow Goblins are in the Valley!" The trees and the bushes took up the cry, and the flowers and the grasses and the animals and the waters passed it on, and by midnight the evil tidings had spread throughout the Valley.

The goblins could hardly contain their excitement. "Soon all the colours of the rainbow will be ours," Yellow gloated. "We'll snatch it as it rises," said Green, "when the colours are still fresh and creamy." The Blue Goblin cackled, "Look at the roots dangling from the walls. They're straining to hear our plans. A lot of good it will do them, or their friend the Rainbow."

Finally, exhausted by their scheming, the goblins fell asleep. Outside, the moon shone on the mirror-like surface of the water, and its magical light was reflected into the cave.

Then all seven goblins had a wonderful dream—the same wonderful dream about the paradise of Rainbowland, where all you had to do was lie on your back and open your mouth, and the most

succulent colours dripped down your throat.

The dream went on and on, the greedy goblins drank and drank, and at dawn, just as their bellies were about to burst, they were awakened by a distant clap of thunder.

The goblins sprang to their feet and rushed to the mouth of the cave. "A storm, a storm!" Red shouted. "Look how the wind is driving it towards us!" Orange cried.

And all the goblins danced and pranced about in glee, for they knew that after the wildest morning thunderstorm comes the most beautiful rainbow.

Yellow was so proud of his plan of attack that he went over it again, while each goblin tested his lasso. "Red, don't forget that you must seize the left flank." "And I move in on the right," the Violet Goblin burst out excitedly. Before the last roll of thunder had faded from the Valley the goblins took up their pails and lassos and marched single file out of the cave.

The sight that greeted them when they reached the meadow

took their breath away. The rising arch of the Rainbow, so rich with colour and promise, almost blinded them. Trembling with excitement, Yellow finally managed to give the signal to attack.

The goblins swung their lassos around and around, and hurled them into the sky. But in that same instant the Rainbow vanished, as if it had been swallowed up by the earth. The goblins were dumbfounded. Nothing like this had ever happened to them before.

They stared up at their empty outstretched lassos . . . which a second later snapped back at them. Indigo wept, Blue cursed, Yellow stumbled, Orange cried out, "Treachery!" Violet tumbled to the grass, Red raged; but the more they thrashed about, the more tangled up they became in their own lassos, until they had snarled themselves into a grunting, groaning mass of goblins on the ground.

As they lay there helplessly, a flood of colours poured forth from all the flowers of the meadow. "The flowers," screamed the Blue Goblin, "the flowers!" He had suddenly remembered the dangling

roots he had made fun of in the cave. Through their roots the flowers had heard the goblins' plans, and they had devised a counter-plan to save the Rainbow. The moment the attack was launched, the flowers had drained the colours of the rainbow into their petals, and as soon as the goblins became ensnared in their own lassos, the petals had let loose the deluge.

So the goblins drowned in the colours they had come to steal, and no one in the valley wept for them.

The Rainbow itself was reborn more magnificently than ever. Out of gratitude, it lifted up the flowers that had saved it and transformed them into glittering dragonflies and butterflies and spendidly plumed birds.

But since that time the Rainbow has become more cautious. Now when it arches across the sky it is careful not to touch the earth anywhere. No matter how you try to sneak up on it, you can never come to the place where it begins or ends.

LOOK TO THE RAINBOW

by E.Y. Harburg

On the day I was born, said my father, said he,
I've an elegant legacy waitin' for ye,
'Tis a rhyme for your lips and a song for your heart,
To sing it whenever the world falls apart.

Look, look, look to the rainbow,
Follow it over the hill and stream.
Look, look, look to the rainbow,
Follow the fellow who follows a dream.

'Twas a sumptious gift to bequeath to a child,
Oh the lure of that song kept her feet runnin' wild.
For you never grow old and you never stand still,
With whippoorwills singing beyond the next hill.

Look, look, look to the rainbow,
Follow it over the hill and stream.
Look, look, look to the rainbow,
Follow the fellow who follows a dream.

So I bundled me heart and I roamed the world free,
To the east, with the lark, to the west with the sea;
And I searched all the earth and I scanned all the skies,
But I found it at last in my own true love's eyes.

Look, look, look to the rainbow,
Follow it over the hill and stream.
Look, look, look to the rainbow,
Follow the fellow who follows a dream.

from

THE WIZARD OF OZ

by L. Frank Baum

In the midst of a tornado Dorothy and her dog, Toto, have been trans-ported to the magical land of Oz. She must seek the help of the Wizard who lives in the Emerald City in order to return home to Kansas. She quickly makes some friends who also need favours from the wizard and together they set off on the yellow brick road.

For some time Dorothy, the Tin Woodman, the Scarecrow and Toto had been walking through the thick woods. The road was still paved with yellow bricks, but these were much covered by dried branches and dead leaves from the trees, and the walking was not at all good.

There were few birds in this part of the forest, for birds love the open country where there is plenty of sunshine; but now and then there came a deep growl from some wild animal hidden among the trees. These sounds made the little girl's heart beat fast, for she did not know what made them; but Toto knew, and he walked close to Dorothy's side and did not even bark in return.

"How long will it be," the child asked of the Tin Woodman, "before we are out of the forest?"

"I cannot tell," was the answer, "for I have never been to the Emerald City. But my father went there once when I was a boy, and he said it was a long journey through dangerous country, although nearer to the city where Oz dwells the country is beautiful. But I am not afraid so long as I have my oil-can, and nothing can hurt the Scarecrow, while you bear upon your forehead the mark of the Good Witch's kiss and that will protect you from harm."

"But Toto!" said the girl anxiously. "What will protect him?"

"We must protect him ourselves if he is in danger," replied the Tin Woodman.

Just as he spoke, there came from the forest a terrible roar, and the next moment a great Lion bounded into the road. With one blow

of his paw he sent the Scarecrow spinning over and over to the edge of the road, and then he struck at the Tin Woodman with his sharp claws. But, to the Lion's surprise, he could make no impression on the tin, although the Woodman fell over in the road and lay still.

Little Toto, now that he had an enemy to face, ran barking towards the Lion, and the great beast had opened his mouth to bite the dog when Dorothy, fearing Toto would be killed, and heedless of danger, rushed forward and slapped the Lion upon his nose as hard as she could, while she cried out: "Don't you dare to bite Toto! You ought to be ashamed of yourself, a big beast like you, to bite a poor little dog!"

"I didn't bite him," said the Lion, as he rubbed his nose with his paw where Dorothy had hit it.

"No, but you tried to," she retorted. "You are nothing but a big coward."

"I know it," said the Lion, hanging his head in shame. "I've always known it. But how can I help it?"

"I don't know, I'm sure. To think of your striking a stuffed man like the poor Scarecrow!"

"Is he stuffed?" asked the Lion in surprise, as he watched her pick up the Scarecrow and set him upon his feet, while she patted him into shape again.

"Of course he's stuffed," replied Dorothy, who was still angry.

"That's why he went over so easily," remarked the Lion. "It astonished me to see him whirl around so. Is the other one stuffed also?"

"No," said Dorothy, "he's made of tin." And she helped the Woodman up again.

"That's why he nearly blunted my claws," said the Lion. "When they scratched against the tin, it made a cold shiver run down my back. What is that little animal you are so tender of?"

"He is my dog, Toto," answered Dorothy.

"Is he made of tin, or stuffed?" asked the Lion.

"Neither. He's a—a—a meat dog," said the girl.

"Oh. He's a curious animal and seems remarkably small now

that I look at him. No one would think of biting such a little thing except a coward like me," continued the Lion sadly.

"What makes you a coward?" asked Dorothy, looking at the great beast in wonder, for he was as big as a small horse.

"It's a mystery," replied the Lion. "I suppose I was born that way. All the other animals in the forest naturally expect me to be brave, for the lion is everywhere thought to be the King of Beasts. I learned that if I roared very loudly, every living thing was frightened and got out of my way. Whenever I've met a man, I've been awfully scared; but I just roared at him, and he has always run away as fast as he could go. If the elephants and the tigers and the bears had ever tried to fight me, I should have run myself—I'm such a coward; but just as soon as they hear me roar, they all try to get away from me, and of course I let them go."

"But that isn't right. The King of the Beasts shouldn't be a coward," said the Scarecrow.

"I know it," returned the Lion, wiping a tear from his eye with the tip of his tail. "It is my great sorrow, and makes my life very unhappy. But whenever there is danger, my heart begins to beat fast."

"Perhaps you have heart disease," said the Tin Woodman.

"It may be," said the Lion.

"If you have," continued the Tin Woodman, "you ought to be glad, for it proves you have a heart. For my part I have no heart, so I cannot have heart disease."

"Perhaps," said the Lion thoughtfully, "if I had no heart I should not be a coward."

"Have you brains?" asked the Scarecrow.

"I suppose so. I've never looked to see," replied the Lion.

"I am going to the Great Oz to ask him to give me some," remarked the Scarecrow, "for my head is stuffed with straw."

"And I am going to ask him to give me a heart," said the Woodman.

"And I am going to ask him to send Toto and me back to Kansas," added Dorothy.

"Do you think Oz could give me courage?" asked the Cowardly Lion.

"Just as easily as he could give me brains," said the Scarecrow.

"Or give me a heart," said the Tin Woodman.

"Or send me back to Kansas," said Dorothy.

"Then if you don't mind, I'll go with you," said the Lion, "for my life is simply unbearable without a bit of courage."

"You will be very welcome," answered Dorothy, "for you will help keep away other wild beasts. It seems to me they must be more cowardly than you are if they allow you to scare them so easily."

"They really are," said the Lion; "but that doesn't make me any braver, and as long as I know myself to be a coward, I shall be unhappy."

So once more the little company set off upon the journey, the Lion walking with stately strides at Dorothy's side. Toto did not approve of this new comrade at first, for he could not forget how he had nearly been crushed between the Lion's great jaws; but after a time, he became more at ease, and presently Toto and the Cowardly Lion had grown to be good friends.

IF I ONLY HAD A BRAIN

Songs by E.Y. Harburg

Scarecrow:

I could while away the hours conferrin' with the flowers
Consultin' with the rain
And my head I'd be scratchin' while my thoughts were busy hatchin'
If I only had a brain.

I'd unravel every riddle for any individle
In trouble or in pain
With the thoughts I'd be thinkin' I could be another Lincoln
If I only had a brain.

Oh, I could tell you why the ocean's near the shore,
I could think of things I never thunk before
And then I'd sit and think some more

I would not be just a nuffin' my head all full of stuffin'
My heart all full of pain
And perhaps I'd deserve you and be even worthy erv you
If I only had a brain.

OVER THE RAINBOW

Somewhere over the rainbow way up high,
There's a land that I heard of once in a lullaby,
Somewhere over the rainbow skies are blue,
And the dreams that you dare to dream really do come true.

Someday I'll wish upon a star
And wake up where the clouds are far
Behind me,
Where troubles melt like lemon drops
Away above the chimney tops
That's where you'll find me.

Somewhere over the rainbow bluebirds fly,
Birds fly over the rainbow, why then, oh why can't I?
If happy little bluebirds fly beyond the rainbow,
Why oh why can't I?

from

THE MAGICIAN'S NEPHEW
by C.S. Lewis

Polly Plummer and her friend Digory go exploring in the attic of his house. They find the secret study of Uncle Andrew, who is performing strange experiments. He tricks them into touching magic rings, which transport them to another world.

There was no doubt about the Magic this time. Down and down they rushed, first through darkness and then through a mass of vague and whirling shapes which might have been almost anything. It grew lighter. Then suddenly they felt that they were standing on something solid. A moment later everything came into focus and they were able to look about them.

"What a queer place!" said Digory.

"I don't like it," said Polly with something like a shudder.

What they noticed first was the light. It wasn't like sunlight, and it wasn't like electric light, or lamps, or candles, or any other light they had ever seen. It was a dull, rather red light, not at all cheerful. It was steady and did not flicker. They were standing on a flat paved surface and buildings rose all around them. There was no roof overhead; they were in a sort of courtyard. The sky was extraordinarily dark—a blue that was almost black. When you had seen that sky you wondered that there should be any light at all.

"It's very funny weather here," said Digory. "I wonder if we've arrived just in time for a thunderstorm; or an eclipse."

"I don't like it," said Polly.

Both of them, without quite knowing why, were talking in whispers. And though there was no reason why they should still go on holding hands after their jump, they didn't let go.

The walls rose very high all around that courtyard. They had many great windows in them, windows without glass, through which you saw nothing but black darkness. Lower down there were great

pillared arches, yawning blackly like the mouths of railway tunnels. It was rather cold.

The stone of which everything was built seemed to be red, but that might only be because of the curious light. It was obviously very old. Many of the flat stones that paved the courtyard had cracks across them. None of them fitted closely together and the sharp corners were all worn off. One of the arched doorways was half filled up with rubble. The two children kept on turning round and round to look at the different sides of the courtyard. One reason was that they were afraid of somebody—or something—looking out of those windows at them when their backs were turned.

"Do you think anyone lives here?" said Digory at last, still in a whisper.

"No," said Polly. "It's all in ruins. We haven't heard a sound since we came."

"Let's stand still and listen for a bit," suggested Digory.

They stood still and listened, but all they could hear was the thump-thump of their own hearts. This place was at least as quiet as the quiet Wood between the Worlds. But it was a different kind of quietness. The silence of the Wood had been rich and warm (you could almost hear the trees growing) and full of life: this was a dead, cold, empty silence. You couldn't imagine anything growing in it.

"Let's go home," said Polly.

"But we haven't seen anything yet," said Digory. "Now we're here, we simply must have a look round."

"I'm sure there's nothing at all interesting here."

"There's not much point in finding a magic ring that lets you into other worlds if you're afraid to look at them when you've got there."

"Who's talking about being afraid?" said Polly, letting go of Digory's hand.

"I only thought you didn't seem very keen on exploring this place."

"I'll go anywhere you go."

"We can get away the moment we want to," said Digory. "Let's take off our green rings and put them in our right-hand pockets. All we've got to do is to remember that our yellows are in our left-hand pockets. You can keep your hand as near your pocket as you like, but don't put it in or you'll touch your yellow and vanish."

They did this and went quietly up to one of the big arched doorways which led into the inside of the building. And when they stood on the threshold and could look in, they saw it was not so dark inside as they had thought at first. It led into a vast, shadowy hall which appeared to be empty; but on the far side there was a row of pillars with arches between them and through those arches there streamed in some more of the same tired-looking light. They crossed the hall, walking very carefully for fear of holes in the floor or of anything lying about that they might trip over. It seemed a long walk. When they had reached the other side they came out through the arches and found themselves in another and larger courtyard.

"That doesn't look very safe," said Polly, pointing at a place where the wall bulged outward and looked as if it were ready to fall over into the courtyard. In one place a pillar was missing between two arches and the bit that came down to where the top of the pillar ought to have been hung there with nothing to support it. Clearly, the place had been deserted for hundreds, perhaps thousands, of years.

"If it's lasted till now, I suppose it'll last a bit longer," said Digory. "But we must be very quiet. You know a noise sometimes brings things down—like an avalanche in the Alps."

They went out of that courtyard into another doorway, and up a great flight of steps and through vast rooms that opened out of one another till you were dizzy with the mere size of the place. Every now and then they thought they were going to get out in the open and see what sort of country lay around the enormous palace. But each time they only got into another courtyard. They must have been magnificent places when people were still living there. In one there had once been a fountain. A great stone monster with wide-spread wings stood with its mouth open and you could still see a bit of piping at the back of its mouth, out of which the water used to pour. Under it was a wide stone basin to hold the water; but it was as dry as a bone. In other places there were the dry sticks of some sort of climbing plant which had wound itself round the pillars and helped to pull some of them down. But it had died long ago. And there were no ants or spiders or any other living things you expect to see in a ruin; and where the dry earth showed between the broken flagstones there was no grass or moss.

It was all so dreary and all so much the same that even Digory was thinking they had better put on their yellow rings and get back to the warm, green, living forest of the in-between place, when they came to two huge doors of some metal that might possibly be gold. One stood a little ajar. So of course they went to look in. Both started back and drew a long breath: for here at last was something worth seeing.

For a second they thought the room was full of people—hundreds of people, all seated, and all perfectly still. Polly and Digory, as you may guess, stood perfectly still themselves for a good long time, looking in. But presently they decided that what they were looking at could not be real people. There was not a movement nor the sound of a breath among them all. They were like the most wonderful waxworks you ever saw.

This time Polly took the lead. There was something in this room which interested her more than it interested Digory: all the figures were wearing magnificent clothes. If you were interested in clothes at all, you could hardly help going in to see them closer. And the blaze of their colours made this room look, not exactly cheerful, but at any rate rich and majestic after all the dust and emptiness of the others. It had more windows, too, and was a good deal lighter.

I can hardly describe the clothes. The figures were all robed and had crowns on their heads. Their robes were of crimson and silvery grey and deep purple and vivid green: and there were patterns, and pictures of flowers and strange beasts, in needlework all over them. Precious stones of astonishing size and brightness stared from their crowns and hung in chains round their necks and peeped out from all the places where anything was fastened.

"Why haven't these clothes all rotted away long ago?" asked Polly.

"Magic," whispered Digory. "Can't you feel it? I bet this whole room is just stiff with enchantments. I could feel it the moment we came in."

"Any one of these dresses would costs hundreds of pounds," said Polly.

But Digory was more interested in the faces, and indeed these were well worth looking at. The people sat in their stone chairs on each side of the room and the floor was left free down the middle. You could walk down and look at the faces in turn.

"They were *nice* people, I think," said Digory.

Polly nodded. All the faces they could see were certainly nice. Both the men and women looked kind and wise, and they seemed to come of a handsome race. But after the children had gone a few steps down the room they came to faces that looked a little different. These were very solemn faces. You felt you would have to mind your P's and Q's, if you ever met living people who looked like that. When they had gone a little further, they found themselves among faces they didn't like: this was about the middle of the room. The faces here looked very strong and proud and happy, but they looked cruel. A little further on they looked crueller. Further on again, they were still cruel but they no longer looked happy. They were even despairing faces: as if the people they belonged to had done dreadful things and also suffered dreadful things. The last figure of all was the most interesting—a woman even more richly dressed than the others, very tall (but every figure in that room was taller than the people of our world), with a look of such fierceness and pride that it took your breath away. Yet she was beautiful too. Years afterward when he was an old man, Digory said he had never in all his life known a woman so beautiful. It is only fair to add that Polly always said she couldn't see anything specially beautiful about her.

This woman, as I said, was the last: but there were plenty of empty chairs beyond her, as if the room had been intended for a much larger collection of images.

"I do wish we knew the story that's behind all this," said Digory. "Let's go back and look at that table sort of thing in the middle of the room."

The thing in the middle of the room was not exactly a table. It was a square pillar about four feet high and on it there rose a little golden arch from which there hung a little golden bell; and beside this there lay a little golden hammer to hit the bell with.

"I wonder . . . I wonder . . . I wonder . . . " said Digory.

"There seems to be something written here," said Polly, stooping down and looking at the side of the pillar.

"By gum, so there is," said Digory. "But of course we shan't be able to read it."

"Shan't we? I'm not so sure," said Polly.

They both looked at it hard and, as you might have expected, the letters cut in the stone were strange. But now a great wonder happened: for, as they looked, though the shape of the strange letters never altered, they found that they could understand them. If only Digory had remembered what he himself had said a few minutes ago, that this was an enchanted room, he might have guessed that the enchantment was beginning to work. But he was too wild with curiosity to think about that. He was longing more and more to know what was written on the pillar. And very soon they both knew. What it said was something like this—at least this is the sense of it though the poetry, when you read it there, was better:

> *Make your choice, adventurous Stranger;*
> *Strike the bell and bide the danger,*
> *Or wonder, till it drives you mad,*
> *What would have followed if you had.*

"No fear!" said Polly. "We don't want any danger."

"Oh but don't you see it's no good!" said Digory. "We can't get out of it now. We shall always be wondering what would have happened if we had struck the bell. I'm not going home to be driven mad by always thinking of that. No fear!"

"Don't be so silly," said Polly. "As if anyone would! What does it matter what would have happened?"

"I expect anyone who's come as far as this is bound to go on wondering till it sends him dotty. That's the Magic of it, you see. I can feel it beginning to work on me already."

"Well, I don't," said Polly crossly. "And I don't believe you do either. You're just putting it on."

"That's all *you* know," said Digory. "It's because you're a girl. Girls never want to know anything but gossip and rot about people getting engaged."

"You looked exactly like your uncle when you said that," said Polly.

"Why can't you keep to the point?" said Digory. "What we're talking about is—"

"How exactly like a man!" said Polly in a very grown-up voice; but she added hastily, in her real voice, "And don't say I'm just like a woman, or you'll be a beastly copy-cat."

"I should never dream of calling a kid like you a woman," said Digory loftily.

"Oh, I'm a kid, am I?" said Polly, who was now in a real rage. "Well you needn't be bothered by having a kid with you any longer then. I'm off. I've had enough of this place. And I've had enough of you too—you beastly, stuck-up, obstinate pig!"

"None of that!" said Digory in a voice even nastier than he meant it to be; for he saw Polly's hand moving to her pocket to get hold of her yellow ring. I can't excuse what he did next except by saying that he was very sorry for it afterwards (and so were a good many other people). Before Polly's hand reached her pocket, he grabbed her wrist, leaning across her with his back against her chest. Then, keeping her other arm out of the way with his other elbow, he leaned forward, picked up the hammer, and struck the golden bell a light, smart tap. Then he let her go and they fell apart staring at each other and breathing hard. Polly was just beginning to cry, not with fear, and not even because he had hurt her wrist quite fairly bad, but with furious anger. Within two seconds, however, they had

something to think about that drove their own quarrels quite out of their minds.

As soon as the bell was struck it gave out a note, a sweet note such as you might have expected, and not very loud. But instead of dying away again, it went on; and as it went on it grew louder. Before a minute had passed it was twice as loud as it had been to begin with. It was soon so loud that if the children had tried to speak (but they weren't thinking of speaking now—they were just standing with their mouths open) they would not have heard one another. Very soon it was so loud that they could not have heard one another even by shouting. And still it grew: all on one note, a continuous sweet sound, though the sweetness had something horrible about it, till all the air in the great room was throbbing with it and they could feel the stone floor trembling under their feet. Then at last it began to be mixed with another sound, a vague, disastrous noise which sounded first like the roar of a distant train, and then like the crash of a falling tree. They heard something like great weights falling. Finally, with a sudden rush and thunder, and a shake that nearly flung them off their feet, about a quarter of the roof at one end of the room fell in, great blocks of masonry fell all round them, and the walls rocked. The noise of the bell stopped. The clouds of dust cleared away. Everything became quiet again.

It was never found out whether the fall of the roof was due to Magic or whether that unbearably loud sound from the bell just happened to strike the note which was more than those crumbling walls could stand.

"There! I hope you're satisfied now," panted Polly.

"Well, it's all over, anyway," said Digory.

And both thought it was; but they had never been more mistaken in their lives.

WALKING
(FOR BETTY)

There goes Betty Binns
Walking in her sleep;
Down the stairs, across the floor,
Down the hall and out the door,
Along the walk and through the gate,
Walking in her sleep.

There goes Betty Binns
Talking in her sleep;
She says hello to Mrs. Brown,
To Mr. Brown and Miss Brown,
"Hello, hello," to all the Browns,
Talking in her sleep.

There goes Betty Binns
Walking in her sleep;
Up one street and down the other
Followed by her anxious mother
(They told her not to stop her daughter
Walking in her sleep).

There goes Betty Binns
Walking in her sleep;
And Mr. Binns and Mrs. Binns
(With slippers on and hair in pins)
And Loey Binns and Teddy Binns
Walking after Betty Binns
Walking in her sleep.

Poems by Lois Simmie

CAREFUL CONNIE

Careful Connie's terrified
Of accidents and ills,
Of gyms and germs and things that squirm,
Heights and depths and heat and chills;
Of bicycles and buses,
Cats and cows and lakes and hills,
Flying things and furry things;

So Careful Connie never will . . .

Climb a tree	might fall down
Go swimming	might drown
Play in the rain	might get muddy
Play games	might get bloody
Cross the street	might get hit
Pet a dog	might get bit
Eat candy	might get a toothache
Eat pizza	might get a bellyache
Read a book	might ruin her eyes
Say hello	might have to say good-bye

Careful Connie's oh so carefully
Sitting in her room,
She's absolutely safe there,
Just sitting in the gloom.
She never laughs and never cries,
She never falls and bumps her head,
She's going to live forever
But she might as well be . . .

Josephine Calico
(FOR MY CAT, JOSIE)

My cat is white and orange and black
And pink and golden-green;
If you see a cat that looks like that,
Her name is Josephine.
Her coat is a glossy orange and black,
Her paws and whiskers are white,
The pupils that float in her shiny eyes
Are as black as a starry night.
Her eyes are the golden-green of leaves
When they are very young,
The pink of a peony's something like
Her rough and gentle tongue
You are the luckiest kid around
And you already know it, I think,
If your cat is black and orange and white
And gold and green and pink.

Attic Fanatic

As I lie in my bed
Things scratch overhead,
They rustle and scrabble and scurry;
And I've got a feeling
That over the ceiling
Are things that are scaly and furry.

Dad says they're just bats,
I see pythons and rats,
Grizzlies and starved alligators;
Dragony things
With claws, fangs and wings . . .

OH PLEASE CALL THE EXTERMINATOR!!!!!!!!

Poems by Lois Simmie

THE GARDEN OF ABDUL GASAZI

by Chris Van Allsburg

Six times Miss Hester's dog Fritz had bitten dear cousin Eunice. So when Miss Hester received an invitation to visit Eunice she was not surprised to read "P.S., Please leave your dog home." On the day of her visit Miss Hester asked young Alan Mitz to stay with Fritz and give him his afternoon walk.

As soon as Miss Hester left, Fritz ran into the parlour. He loved to chew on the chairs and shake the stuffing out of the pillows. But Alan was ready. All morning long he kept Fritz from sinking his sharp little teeth into the furniture. Finally the dog gave up and fell asleep, exhausted. Alan took a nap, too, but first he hid his hat under his shirt, hats being one of Fritz's favourite things to chew.

An hour later Alan quickly awoke when Fritz gave him a bite on the nose. The bad-mannered dog was ready for his afternoon walk. Alan fastened Fritz's leash and the dog dragged him out of the house. Walking along, they discovered a small white bridge at the side of the road. Alan decided to let Fritz lead the way across.

Some distance beyond the bridge Alan stopped to read a sign. It said: ABSOLUTELY, POSITIVELY NO DOGS ALLOWED IN THIS GARDEN. At the bottom it was signed: ABDUL GASAZI, RETIRED MAGICIAN. Behind the sign stood a vine-covered wall with an open doorway. Alan took the warning quite seriously. He turned to leave, but as he did, Fritz gave a tremendous tug, and snapped right out of his collar. He bolted straight ahead through the open door, with Alan running right behind.

"Fritz, stop, you bad dog!" cried Alan, but the dog simply ignored him. Down shadowed paths and across sunlit lawns they raced, deeper and deeper into the garden. Finally, Alan drew close enough to grab hold of Fritz. But as he reached out he slipped and fell. Fritz barked with laughter as he galloped out of sight. Alan slowly picked himself up. He knew he had to find Fritz before Mr. Gasazi discovered him. Bruised and tired, he hurried off in the dog's direction.

After a long search Alan was ready to give up. He was afraid he might never find Fritz. But then he came upon fresh dog prints.

Slowly he followed Fritz's tracks along a path that led into a forest. The dirt path ended and a brick wall began. There were no more tracks to follow, but Alan was certain that Fritz must be just ahead.

Alan started running. In front of him he could see a clearing in the forest. As he came dashing out of the woods he stopped as quickly as if he had run up against a wall. For there, in front of him, stood a truly awesome sight. It was the house of Gasazi. Alan nervously climbed the great stairs, convinced Fritz had come this way and been captured.

The boy's heart was pounding when he arrived at the huge door. He took a deep breath and reached for the bell, but before he touched it the door swung open. There, in the shadow of the hallway, stood Gasazi the Great. "Greetings, do come in" was all that he said.

Alan followed Gasazi into a large room. When the magician turned around Alan quickly apologized for letting Fritz into the garden. He politely asked that, if Mr. Gasazi had Fritz, would he

please give him back? The magician listened carefully and then, smiling, said, "Certainly you may have your little Fritzie. Follow me." With those words he went to the door and led Alan back outside.

They were walking across the lawn when suddenly Gasazi stopped by a gathering of ducks. He began to speak in a voice that was more like a growl. "I detest dogs. They dig up my flowers, they chew on my trees. Do you know what I do to dogs I find in my garden?" "What?" whispered Alan, almost afraid to hear the answer. "I TURN THEM INTO DUCKS!" bellowed Gasazi. In horror, Alan looked at the birds in front of him. When one duck came forward, Gasazi said, "There's your Fritz." Alan begged the magician to change Fritz back. "Impossible," he answered, "only time can do that. This spell may last years or perhaps just a day. Now take your dear bird and please don't come again."

When Alan took the bird in his arms it tried to give him a bite. "Good old boy," said Alan sadly as he patted the bird on the head.

"You really haven't changed so much." With tears in his eyes he
started for home. Behind him Alan could hear Gasazi laughing. As
he approached the stairway, a gust of wind took Alan's hat sailing
right off his head. Running along with one arm reaching for the hat,
Alan lost his hold on Fritz. The duck flew out ahead and grabbed
the hat in midair. But instead of landing he just kept on flying,
higher and higher, until he disappeared in the afternoon clouds.

Alan just stood and stared at the empty sky. "Good-bye, old
fellow," he called out sadly, sure that Fritz was gone forever. At
least he had something to chew on. Slowly, one step after another,
Alan found his way back to the garden gate and over the bridge. It
was sunset by the time he reached Miss Hester's. Lights were on
and he knew she must be home. With a heavy heart he approached
the door, wondering how Miss Hester would take the news.

When Miss Hester came to the door Alan blurted out his incre-
dible story. He could barely hold back the tears; then racing out of

the kitchen, dog food on his nose, came Fritz. Alan couldn't believe his eyes. "I'm afraid Mr. Gasazi played a trick on you," said Miss Hester, trying to hide a smile. "Fritz was in the front yard when I returned. He must have found his own way home while you were with Mr. Gasazi. You see, Alan, no one can really turn dogs into ducks; that old magician just made you think that duck was Fritz."

Alan felt very silly. He promised himself he'd never be fooled like that again. He was too old to believe in magic. Miss Hester watched from the porch as Alan waved good-bye and hurried down the road to go home. Then she called out to Fritz, who was playfully running around the front yard. He came trotting up the front steps with something in his mouth and dropped it at Miss Hester's feet. "Why you bad dog," she said. "What are you doing with Alan's hat?"

Cloudy With a
Chance of Meatballs

by Judi Barrett

W e were all sitting around the big kitchen table. It was Saturday morning. Pancake morning. Mom was squeezing oranges for juice. Henry and I were betting on how many pancakes we each could eat. And Grandpa was doing the flipping. Seconds later, something flew through the air headed toward the kitchen ceiling . . . and landed right on Henry.

After we realized that the flying object was only a pancake, we all laughed, even Grandpa. Breakfast continued quite uneventfully. All the other pancakes landed in the pan. And all of them were eaten, even the one that landed on Henry.

That night, touched off by the pancake incident at breakfast, Grandpa told us the best tall-tale bedtime story he'd ever told.

Across an ocean, over lots of huge bumpy mountains, across three hot deserts, and one smaller ocean . . . there lay the tiny town of Chewandswallow.

In most ways, it was very much like any other tiny town. It had a Main Street lined with stores, houses with trees and gardens around them, a schoolhouse, about three hundred people, and some assorted cats and dogs.

But there were no food stores in the town of Chewandswallow. They didn't need any. The sky supplied all the food they could possibly want.

The only thing that was really different about Chewandswallow was its weather. It came three times a day, at breakfast, lunch, and dinner. Everything that everyone ate came from the sky.

Whatever the weather served, that was what they ate.

But it never rained. It never showered. And it never blew just wind. It rained things like soup and juice. It snowed mashed potatoes and green peas. And sometimes the wind blew in storms of hamburgers.

The people could watch the weather report on television in the morning and they would even hear a prediction for the next day's food.

When the townspeople went outside, they carried their plates, cups, glasses, forks, spoons, knives and napkins with them. That way they would always be prepared for any kind of weather.

If there were leftovers, and there usually were, the people took them home and put them in their refrigerators in case they got hungry between meals.

The menu varied.

By the time they woke up in the morning, breakfast was coming down.

After a brief shower of orange juice, low clouds of sunny-side-up eggs moved in followed by pieces of toast. Butter and jelly sprinkled down for the toast. And most of the time it rained milk afterwards.

For lunch one day, frankfurters, already in their rolls, blew in from the northwest at about five miles an hour.

There were mustard clouds nearby. Then the wind shifted to the east and brought in baked beans.

A drizzle of soda finished off the meal.

Dinner one night consisted of lamb chops, becoming heavy at times, with occasional ketchup. Periods of peas and baked potatoes were followed by gradual clearing, with a wonderful Jell-O setting in the west.

The Sanitation Department of Chewandswallow had a rather unusual job for a sanitation department. It had to remove the food that fell on the houses and sidewalks and lawns. The workers cleaned things up after every meal and fed all the cats and dogs. Then they emptied some of it into the surrounding oceans for fish and turtles and whales to eat. The rest of the food was put back into the earth so that the soil would be richer for the people's flower gardens.

Life for the townspeople was delicious until the weather took a turn for the worse. One day there was nothing but Gorgonzola cheese all day long.

The next day there was only broccoli, all overcooked.

And the next day there were Brussels sprouts and peanut butter with mayonnaise.

Another day there was a pea soup fog. No one could see where they were going and they could barely find the rest of the meal that got stuck in the fog.

The food was getting larger and larger, and so were the portions. The people were getting frightened. Violent storms blew up frequently. Awful things were happening.

One Tuesday there was a hurricane of bread and rolls all day long and into the night. There were soft rolls and hard rolls, some with seeds and some without. There was white bread and rye and whole wheat toast. Most of it was larger than they had ever seen bread and rolls before. It was a terrible day. Everyone had to stay indoors. Roofs were damaged, and the sanitation department was beside itself. The mess took the workers four days to clean up, and the sea was full of floating rolls.

To help out, the people piled up as much bread as they could in their backyards. The birds picked at it a bit, but it just stayed there and got staler and staler.

There was a storm of pancakes one morning and a downpour of maple syrup that nearly flooded the town. A huge pancake covered the school. No one could get it off because of its weight, so they had to close the school.

Lunch one day brought fifteen-inch drifts of cream cheese and jelly sandwiches. Everyone ate themselves sick and the day ended with a stomach ache.

There was an awful salt and pepper wind accompanied by an even worse tomato tornado. People were sneezing themselves silly and running to avoid tomatoes. The town was a mess. There were seeds and pulp everywhere.

The Sanitation Department gave up. The job was too big.

Everyone feared for their lives. They couldn't go outside most of the time. Many houses had been badly damaged by giant meatballs, stores were boarded up and there was no more school for the children.

So a decision was made to abandon the town of Chewandswallow. It was a matter of survival.

The people glued together the giant pieces of stale bread sandwich-style with peanut butter . . . took the absolute necessities with them, and set sail on their rafts for a new land.

After being afloat for a week, they finally reached a small coastal town, which welcomed them. The bread had held up surprisingly well, well enough for them to build temporary houses for themselves out of it.

The children began school again, and the adults all tried to find places for themselves in the new land. The biggest change they had to make was getting used to buying food at a supermarket. They found it odd that the food was kept on shelves, packaged in boxes, cans and bottles. Meat that had to be cooked was kept in large refrigerators. Nothing came down from the sky except rain and snow. The clouds above their heads were not made of fried eggs. No one ever got hit by a hamburger again.

And nobody dared to go back to Chewandswallow to find out what had happened to it. They were too afraid.

Henry and I were awake until the very end of Grandpa's story. I remember his goodnight kiss.

The next morning we woke up to see snow falling outside our window.

We ran downstairs for breakfast and ate it a little faster than usual so we could go sledding with Grandpa.

It's funny, but even as we were sliding down the hill we thought we saw a giant pat of butter at the top, and we could almost smell mashed potatoes.

A WHOPPER

A storm blew the feathers off a chicken and the chipmunks out of their holes.

It also forced the birds to fly backward to keep the sand out of their eyes.

It also saved a rabbit's life. When a fox came after him, the rabbit put up his ears which caught the wind like a pair of sails. And it blew him away.

But in some places that storm
did even stranger things.
It blew the cracks out of a fence,
and the teeth out of a saw,
and a well out of the ground,
which the farmer
then turned upside down
and used as a silo.

It also moved a township line,
and changed the time of day
and the day of the week,
and kept the sun from setting
for three hours
and forty-five minutes.

It also blew the hair off a man's head,
and the whiskers off his face,
and the shoes off his socks,
and the socks off his feet.

Many people who ventured out that day
were blown up against brick walls,
then flattened by the wind
thin as this page,
then peeled off by a businessman
and sold as circus posters.

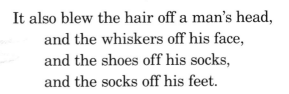

When that storm was at its worst, one person made the mistake of opening his mouth. Before he knew it, he had swallowed five barrels of air, which blew him up to five times his normal size, which caused him to bounce like a tennis ball.

LOOK THROUGH MY WINDOW

Everyone needs to have family and friends. If you have ever moved to a new school, you know how difficult it is to break into a new circle of friends. Families can also change shape when they move far away from other relatives, or through divorce, or perhaps even because of the death of a loved one. We constantly have to change our relationships and make new ones. It is very important to remember our family and friends from the past, to know we belong to a circle of people, then and now. In this excerpt, two girls who have a special relationship receive similar gifts that will have a different meaning for each of them.

At last the presents! So many, such wonderful presents! Emily opened a puppet John had made for her, a new dress from her parents, Harriet the Spy *from Mr. Bloomfield and* The Long Secret *from Kate's mother, a hand mirror from Sophie, a five-cent package of Kleenex tissues and some Lifesavers from James. He had given everyone the same presents.*

"Two each," he boasted happily, basking in their laughter.

"Here." Dad handed Kate and Emily identical boxes.

" 'With affection from your neighbour, Anne Thurstone,' "
Emily puzzled out the crabbed writing. She undid the wrapping
carefully. Both of them had been given lockets which had been
Mrs. Thurstone's when she was a girl.

"Time they belonged to young things again," she barked.

Emily's had butterfly wings inside it. It shimmered and
changed colour when she moved it. She thought she had never
seen anything more beautiful.

(from *Look Through My Window*, by Jean Little)

Do you have things that remind you of someone you used to know,
or that have been handed down over the years? Memories of people
who were important in our lives help us build new relationships as
we change and grow.

You can look through life's window at the relationships in your
past, and then try to glimpse what may happen in your future.

TAKING CARE OF CRUMLEY

by Ted Staunton

When it all began, I was hanging upside down. Suddenly the jungle gym shook. It got dark all around and I was looking at Ugly Augie Crumley and his Goons—the biggest bullies in school. Was I ever scared!

Ugly Augie smiled. He liked to scare kids. He pushed me, pinched me, poked me, pulled my ears, and just plain picked on me. Then they left me with my shoes tied to the bars and a promise to pick on me a whole lot more.

As soon as I got free, I went to see Maggie, the Greenapple Street genius.

"Can you make Ugly Augie stop bugging me?" I asked. Maggie laughed. "No problem, Cyril. But . . . you'll have to do anything I say."

"No way!" I said.

Then I remembered Ugly Augie's promise.

"O.K.," I sighed.

"Good," said Maggie. "Tomorrow I'll take care of Crumley. This is going to be fun!"

The next day was Friday. Maggie came down Greenapple Street and told me a Perfectly Perfect Plan. I had to tell a lie to Ugly Augie without anyone else hearing. When I got to school, I snuck up to Ugly Augie and whispered, "Crumley, you're going to get it!" It felt nice to say.

A little louder I said, "My cousin Vern, who is in Grade 7 and plays football, is coming after school to make you into mush with one hand!" That felt even nicer.

I shouted, "He'll make you look like a hockey puck!" Then I roared, "You're all washed up, bozo!" and walked away like a big hero.

Maggie said that Ugly Augie was just a bully who was chicken

inside. After school he would run home so fast that he'd never know I didn't have a cousin Vern. I thought my problem was solved.

Sure enough, after school I saw Ugly Augie sneaking off for home. Then I heard the Goons.

"Hey Augie, where are you going?"

"You can beat this guy!" Now I knew why I was supposed to whisper—to keep the Goons away. I got scared all over again. They came around the corner and saw me—all alone. I gulped. They charged, and I ran for my life. Suddenly there was Maggie on her bike.

"Hop on," she shouted, and we took off.

"You're going to pay for lying to me, Cyril," yelled Ugly Augie. "Bring us money on Monday or else!"

I told Maggie, "I forgot to whisper." She moaned. "My best plan ever and you blew it, Cyril. Now I have to start all over, and you have to carry my books. And watch out for the poison ivy around

here." We went home to Greenapple Street and didn't say another word.

I worried all weekend while Maggie sat in her tree thinking. At last, on Sunday, she came down. She was dressed very strangely.

"Cyril," she said, "I have a Terribly Terrific Plan. Open your piggy bank and put all your pennies in this bag." When I was done, she took the bag and headed down the street. "See you tomorrow," was all she said.

Monday morning Maggie was ready.

"Here's the plan," she said. "Tell Ugly Augie you have poison ivy. Then try to give him the bag of pennies. He'll be scared to touch you or your money ever again."

"Not another lie," I groaned. "I don't even have poison ivy."

"No, dummy," said Maggie, "but I'll make you look like you do." When she was finished, Maggie smiled.

"You sure look sick," she said. "Now go do your stuff."

I started to walk, but my knees were knocking. Every penny I owned was in that bag. What if I didn't fool them? I peeked around the corner. Ugly Augie looked awfully ugly that morning. The Goons looked like grumpy gorillas. I got goose bumps all over.

I opened the bag and stuffed some money in my shirt, just in case. Then I walked out to the jungle gym.

Slowly they circled me. My stomach got all squishy. Ugly Augie smiled and said, "Gimme."

"H-h-here," I said. "But I have poison ivy and if you touch me or my stuff you'll get it too!" Ugly Augie stared. Then he rubbed my face.

"Lipstick," he snorted. "This kid always lies." He snatched my

money and in a second they all had some. The Terribly Terrific Plan had turned terrifically terrible.

But when I ran back to Maggie and told her what had happened, she began to laugh.

"It worked, it worked," she whooped. "I knew they'd take the money!"

"What?" I said.

"Yesterday I took your pennies to the field and mushed them up with poison ivy," she said. "Augie and his Goons are going to itch like crazy. And they'll be scared to touch you in case they get even more. I've taken care of Crumley!"

"All right!" I roared, and we danced around. After a minute, I stopped. I felt itchy. Maggie scratched her hands. Then I remembered.

"Oh, no," I said. Slowly I felt inside my shirt. "I kept some of the money," I whispered.

"Eeeek," screeched Maggie. "You dummy. We have poison ivy!"

We itched for a month. Everybody got in trouble for what they did to everybody else, and everybody blamed me.

One day I met Ugly Augie on Greenapple Street. "Oh, oh," I thought, but he ran away.

"You keep away from me, Cyril," he yelled.

I went to the schoolyard. A couple of the Goons were there, but they hid when they saw me.

"Quit picking on us, Cyril," they shouted.

Suddenly everything was all right. Maggie's plan had worked. Ugly Augie had stopped bugging me. We had taken care of Crumley!

TALES FOR
THE PERFECT CHILD

by Florence Parry Heide

RUBY

R uby wanted to go over to Ethel's house to play. But Ruby's mother said, "You have to watch Clyde."

Clyde was Ruby's baby brother. He had just learned to walk.

"I don't want to watch Clyde. I want to go over to Ethel's house to play," said Ruby.

Ruby's mother was tired. She had been watching Clyde all day. "You have to watch Clyde because I have to take a bubble bath," said Ruby's mother. She went into the bathroom.

Ruby called Ethel. "I'll be over in a minute."

Then Ruby watched Clyde.

She watched him take all of the clothes out of all of the drawers in all of the bureaus in all of the rooms.

She watched him take all of the rice and all of the flour and all of the salt and all of the sugar and all of the coffee out of all of the kitchen cupboards and spill it all on the nice clean floor.

She watched him pull the tablecloth off the kitchen table. The

bananas that had been on the table landed on Clyde's head.

Ruby watched Clyde start to cry very loud.

Her mother came out of the bathroom. "What's going on?" she asked. "I told you to watch Clyde."

"I was watching him," said Ruby truthfully. "I was watching him the whole time."

In a few minutes Ruby was ringing Ethel's doorbell. "I told you I'd be over in a minute," she said. "I just had to watch Clyde."

ARTHUR

Arthur liked to wear his old comfortable clothes and his old comfortable sneakers. He did not like to get dressed up. He did not like to wear white shirts and nice suits, and he did not like to wear any of the nice ties he had gotten for his birthday.

"Arthur," said his mother, "we're going to visit Aunt Eunice. Put on your white shirt and your nice suit and your new tie and your nice new shiny shoes."

Arthur did not want to get dressed up. He did not want to visit Aunt Eunice. He wanted to stay home in his old clothes and watch his favourite program.

"I want to stay here in my old clothes and watch my favourite program," said Arthur.

"Well, you're going with me to see Aunt Eunice, and that's that. And you're going to get dressed up, and that's that."

Arthur's mother always wanted to tell Arthur what was what. That was very thoughtful. Mothers are thoughtful people.

"All right," said Arthur.

Arthur's mother was surprised. Usually Arthur argued. Arthur was very good at arguing.

Arthur put on his white shirt and his nice new suit and the tie that Aunt Eunice had given him for his last birthday. He put on the new shiny shoes.

"Now you look like a little gentleman," said his mother.

And he did. He looked like a little gentleman.

As soon as he was all dressed up, Arthur went out to the kitchen. He opened the refrigerator. He poured himself a nice big glass of grape juice. Some of it got on his face, but most of it got on his white shirt and the pretty new suit and the tie that Aunt Eunice had given him for his birthday.

Then he went out to the yard. In a few minutes his nice shiny shoes were all muddy.

His mother was sad.

"Oh, dear," she said. "You've spoiled all your nice clothes. You can't go to see Aunt Eunice looking like that. You'll have to stay home."

So Arthur changed back into his blue jeans and T-shirt and his old comfortable sneakers. His mother went to see Aunt Eunice, and Arthur had to stay home and watch his favourite television program.

PEARLS

Dad gave me a string of pearls for my birthday.
They aren't real pearls but they look real.
They came nested in deep, deep blue velvet in a hinged box
      with a silvery lid.
His sister had some like them when she was my age.
She was thrilled.
He thought I'd really like them.
I said I did.

I love the box.

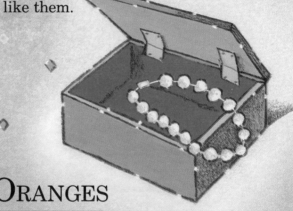

ORANGES

I peel oranges neatly.
The sections come apart cleanly, perfectly, in my hands.
When Emily peels an orange,
She tears holes in it and squirts juice all over.

Emily is my best friend . . .

"I don't see how you do it, Kate," she says.
"It's easy," I tell her.

I hope she never learns how to peel oranges.

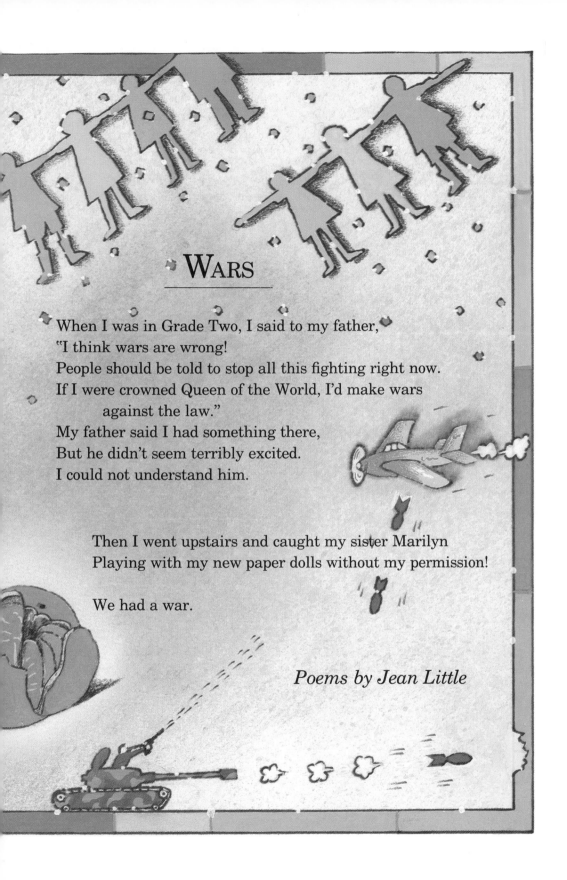

WARS

When I was in Grade Two, I said to my father,
"I think wars are wrong!
People should be told to stop all this fighting right now.
If I were crowned Queen of the World, I'd make wars
      against the law."
My father said I had something there,
But he didn't seem terribly excited.
I could not understand him.

Then I went upstairs and caught my sister Marilyn
Playing with my new paper dolls without my permission!

We had a war.

Poems by Jean Little

LOUISA, LOUISA

by Jean Little

"Would you hold the baby for a moment?" she asked.

So I hold you, Louisa.
I sit very still and I hold you and watch
    you sleep.
You have only been a person for six weeks.
For this moment, you are all mine.
Not that there is much of you!
But your eyelids flutter. I can feel you
    breathing.
You are completely alive, Louisa.
There is so much that you do not know.
You do not know about school!
Do you know about words yet, Louisa?
    No, no words.
You have never heard of computers.
You have never heard of dying, Louisa.

Shhh. Sleep.

You will discover the sun.
You will see Emily laughing.
You will come upon the alphabet and rainbows.
You will ride up an escalator.
You will read *The Secret Garden* for the
    first time.
You will love a boy called Arthur. Or Bill.
You may go to Tibet.
You will get a letter.
You will wear shoes and you will create
    a dance all your own.
Here is a secret, Louisa.
Living is worth schools.
Loving balances computers.
Even dying, and knowing about dying,
    cannot stop your dancing.

But now I am holding you.
And you are sleeping.
Louisa, shhh.
I love you right now, Louisa, before
    you know anything,
Before you even know that you are Louisa.

from

TALES OF A
FOURTH GRADE NOTHING

by Judy Blume

I will never forget Friday, May tenth. It's the most important day of my life. It didn't start out that way. It started out ordinary. I went to school. I ate my lunch. I had gym. And then I walked home from school with Jimmy Fargo. We planned to meet at our special rock in the park as soon as we changed our clothes.

In the elevator I told Henry I was glad summer was coming. Henry said he was too. When I got out at my floor I walked down the hall and opened the door to my apartment. I took off my jacket and hung it in the closet. I put my books on the hall table next to my mother's purse. I went straight to my room to change my clothes and check Dribble.

The first thing I noticed was my chain latch. It was unhooked. My bedroom door was open. And there was a chair right smack in the middle of my doorway. I nearly tumbled over it. I ran to my dresser to check Dribble. He wasn't there! His bowl with the rocks and water was there—but Dribble was gone.

I got really scared. I thought, *Maybe he died while I was at school and I didn't know about it.* So I rushed into the kitchen and hollered, "Mom . . . where's Dribble?" My mother was baking something. My brother sat on the kitchen floor, banging pots and pans together. "Be quiet!" I yelled at Fudge. "I can't hear anything with all that noise."

"What did you say, Peter?" my mother asked me.

"I said I can't find Dribble. Where is he?"

"You mean he's not in his bowl?" my mother asked.

I shook my head.

"Oh dear!" my mother said. "I hope he's not crawling around somewhere. You know I don't like the way he smells. I'm going to have a look in the bedrooms. You check in here, Peter."

My mother hurried off. I looked at my brother. He was smiling.

"Fudge, do you know where Dribble is?" I asked calmly.

Fudge kept smiling.

"Did you take him? Did you, Fudge?" I asked not so calmly.

Fudge giggled and covered his mouth with his hands.

I yelled. "Where is he? What did you do with my turtle?"

No answer from Fudge. He banged his pots and pans together again. I yanked the pots out of his hand. I tried to speak softly. "Now tell me where Dribble is. Just tell me where my turtle is. I won't be mad if you tell me. Come on, Fudge . . . please."

Fudge looked up at me. "In tummy," he said.

"What do you mean, in tummy?" I asked, narrowing my eyes.

"Dribble in tummy!" he repeated.

"What tummy?" I shouted at my brother.

"This one," Fudge said, rubbing his stomach. "Dribble in this tummy! Right here!"

I decided to go along with his game. "Okay. How did he get in there, Fudge?" I asked.

Fudge stood up. He jumped up and down and sang out, "I ATE HIM. . . . ATE HIM . . . ATE HIM!" Then he ran out of the room.

My mother came back into the kitchen. "Well, I just can't find him anywhere," she said. "I looked in all the dresser drawers and the bathroom cabinets and the shower and the tub and . . . "

"Mom," I said, shaking my head. "How could you?"

"How could I what, Peter?" Mom asked.

"How could you let him do it?"

"Let who do what, Peter?" Mom asked.

"LET FUDGE EAT DRIBBLE!" I screamed.

My mother started to mix whatever she was baking. "Don't be silly, Peter," she said. "Dribble is a turtle."

"HE ATE DRIBBLE!" I insisted.

"*Peter Warren Hatcher*! STOP SAYING THAT!" Mom hollered.

"Well, ask him. Go ahead and ask him," I told her.

Fudge was standing in the kitchen doorway with a big grin on his face. My mother picked him up and patted his head. "Fudgie," she said to him, "tell Mommy where brother's turtle is."

"In tummy," Fudge said.

"What tummy?" Mom asked.

"MINE!" Fudge laughed.

My mother put Fudge down on the kitchen counter where he couldn't get away from her. "Oh, you're fooling Mommy . . . right?"

"No fool!" Fudge said.

My mother turned very pale. "You really ate your brother's turtle?"

Big smile from Fudge.

"YOU MEAN THAT YOU PUT HIM IN YOUR MOUTH AND CHEWED HIM UP . . . LIKE THIS?" Mom made believe she was chewing.

"No," Fudge said.

A smile of relief crossed my mother's face. "Of course you didn't. It's just a joke." She put Fudge down on the floor and gave me a *look*.

Fudge babbled. "No chew. No chew. Gulp . . . gulp . . . all gone turtle. Down Fudge's tummy."

Me and my mother stared at Fudge.

"You didn't!" Mom said.

"Did so!" Fudge said.

"No!" Mom shouted.

"Yes!" Fudge shouted back.

"Yes?" Mom asked weakly, holding onto a chair with both hands.

"Yes!" Fudge beamed.

My mother moaned and picked up my brother. "Oh no! My angel! My precious little baby! OH . . . NO . . . "

My mother didn't stop to think about my turtle. She didn't even give Dribble a thought. She didn't even stop to wonder how my turtle liked being swallowed by my brother. She ran to the phone with Fudge tucked under one arm. I followed. Mom dialed the operator and cried, "Oh help! This is an emergency. My baby ate a turtle . . . STOP THAT LAUGHING," my mother told the operator. "Send an ambulance right away; 25 West 68th Street."

Mom hung up. She didn't look too well. Tears were running down her face. She put Fudge down on the floor. I couldn't understand why she was so upset. Fudge seemed just fine.

"Help me, Peter," Mom begged. "Get me blankets."

I ran into my brother's room. I grabbed two blankets from Fudge's bed. He was following me around with that silly grin on his face. I felt like giving him a pinch. How could he stand there looking so happy when he had my turtle inside him?

I delivered the blankets to my mother. She wrapped Fudge up in them and ran to the front door. I followed and grabbed her purse from the hall table. I figured she'd be glad I thought of that.

Out in the hall I pressed the elevator buzzer. We had to wait a few minutes. Mom paced up and down in front of the elevator. Fudge was cradled in her arms. He sucked his fingers and made that slurping noise I like. But all I could think of was Dribble.

Finally, the elevator got to our floor. There were three people in it besides Henry. "This is an emergency," Mom wailed. "The ambulance is waiting downstairs. Please hurry!"

"Yes, Mrs. Hatcher. Of course," Henry said. "I'll run her down just as fast as I can. No other stops."

Someone poked me in the back. I turned around. It was Mrs. Rudder. "What's the matter?" she whispered.

"It's my brother," I whispered back. "He ate my turtle."

Mrs. Rudder whispered *that* to the man next to her and *he* whispered it to the lady next to *him* who whispered it to Henry. I faced front and pretended I didn't hear anything.

My mother turned around with Fudge in her arms and said, "That's not funny. Not funny at all!"

But Fudge said, "Funny, funny, funny Fudgie!"

Everybody laughed. Everybody except my mother.

The elevator door opened. Two men, dressed in white, were waiting with a stretcher. "This the baby!" one of them asked.

"Yes. Yes it is," Mom sobbed.

"Don't worry, lady. We'll be to the hospital in no time."

"Come, Peter," my mother said, tugging at my sleeve. "We're going to ride in the ambulance with Fudge."

My mother and I climbed into the back of the blue ambulance. I was never in one before. It was neat. Fudge kneeled on a cot and peered out through the window. He waved at the crowd of people that had gathered on the sidewalk.

One of the attendants sat in back with us. The other one was driving. "What seems to be the trouble, lady?" the attendant asked. "This kid looks pretty healthy to me."

"He swallowed a turtle," my mother whispered.

"He did WHAT?" the attendant asked.

"Ate my turtle. That's what!" I told him.

My mother covered her face with her hanky and started to cry again.

"Hey, Joe!" the attendant called to the driver. "Make it snappy . . . *this* one swallowed a turtle!"

"That's not funny!" Mom insisted. I didn't think so either, considering it was my turtle!

We arrived at the back door of the hospital. Fudge was whisked away by two nurses. My mother ran after him. "You wait here, young man," another nurse called to me, pointing to a bench.

I sat down on the hard wooden bench. I didn't have anything to do. There weren't any books or magazines spread out, like when I go to Dr. Cone's office. So I watched the clock and read all the signs

on the walls. I found out I was in the emergency section of the hospital.

After a while the nurse came back. She gave me some paper and crayons. "Here you are. Be a good boy and draw some pictures. Your mother will be out soon."

I wondered if she knew about Dribble and that's why she was trying to be nice to me. I didn't feel like drawing any pictures. I wondered what they were doing to Fudge in there. Maybe he wasn't such a bad little guy after all. I remembered that Jimmy Fargo's little cousin once swallowed the most valuable rock from Jimmy's collection. And my mother told me that when I was a little kid I swallowed a quarter. Still . . . a quarter's not a turtle!

I watched the clock on the wall for an hour and ten minutes. Then a door opened and my mother stepped out with Dr. Cone. I was surprised to see him. I didn't know he worked in the hospital.

"Hello, Peter," he said.

"Hello, Dr. Cone. Did you get my turtle?"

"Not yet, Peter," he said. "But I do have something to show you.

Here are some X-rays of your brother."

I studied the X-rays as Dr. Cone pointed things out to me.

"You see," he said. "There's your turtle . . . right there."

I looked hard. "Will Dribble be in there forever?" I asked.

"No. Definitely not! We'll get him out. We gave Fudge some medicine already. That should do the trick nicely."

"What kind of medicine?" I asked. "What trick?"

"Castor oil, Peter," my mother said. "Fudge took castor oil. And milk of magnesia. And prune juice too. Lots of that. All those things will help to get Dribble out of Fudge's tummy."

"We just have to wait," Dr. Cone said. "Probably until tomorrow or the day after. Fudge will have to spend the night here. But I don't think he's going to be swallowing anything that he isn't supposed to be swallowing from now on."

"How about Dribble?" I asked. "Will Dribble be all right?" My mother and Dr. Cone looked at each other. I knew the answer before he shook his head and said, "I think you may have to get a new turtle, Peter."

"I don't want a new turtle!" I said. Tears came to my eyes. I was embarrassed and wiped them away with the back of my hand. Then my nose started to run and I had to sniffle. "I want Dribble," I said. "That's the only turtle I want."

My mother took me home in a taxi. She told me my father was on his way to the hospital to be with Fudge. When we got home she made me lamb chops for dinner, but I wasn't very hungry. My father came home late that night. I was still up. My father looked gloomy. He whispered to my mother, "Not yet . . . not yet."

The next day was Saturday. No school. I spent the whole day in the hospital waiting room. There were plenty of people around. And magazines and books too. It wasn't like the hard bench in the emergency hallway. It was more like a living room. I told everybody that my brother ate my turtle. They looked at me kind of funny. But nobody ever said they were sorry to hear about my turtle. Never once.

My mother joined me for supper in the hospital coffee shop. I

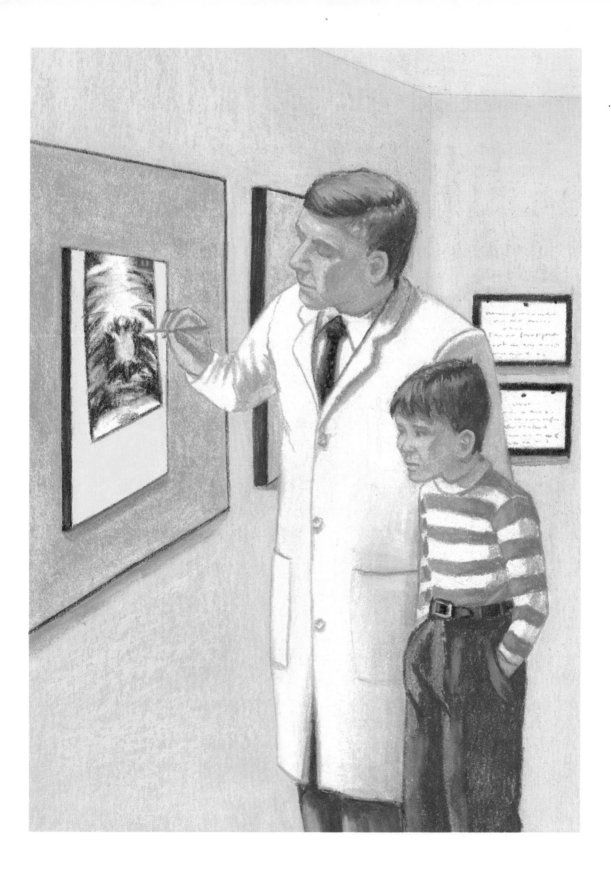

ordered a hamburger but I left most of it. Because right in the middle of supper my mother told me that if the medicine didn't work soon Fudge might have to have an operation to get Dribble out of him. My mother didn't eat anything.

That night my grandmother came to stay with me. My mother and father stayed at the hospital with Fudge. Things were pretty dreary at home. Every hour the phone rang. It was my mother calling from the hospital with a report.

"Not yet . . . I see," Grandma repeated. "Nothing happening yet."

I was miserable. I was lonely. Grandma didn't notice. I even missed Fudge banging his pots and pans together. In the middle of the night the phone rang again. It woke me up and I crept out into the hallway to hear what was going on.

Grandma shouted, "Whoopee! It's out! Good news at last."

She hung up and turned to me. "The medicine finally worked, Peter. All that castor oil and milk of magnesia and prune juice finally worked. The turtle is out!"

"Alive or dead?" I asked.

"PETER WARREN HATCHER, WHAT A QUESTION!" Grandma shouted.

So my brother no longer had a turtle inside of him. And I no longer had a turtle! I didn't like Fudge as much as I thought I did before the phone rang.

The next morning Fudge came home from the hospital. My father carried him into the apartment. My mother's arms were loaded with presents. All for Fudge! My mother put the presents down and kissed him. She said, "Fudgie can have anything he wants. Anything at all. Mommy's so happy her baby's all better!"

It was disgusting. Presents and kisses and attention for Fudge. I couldn't even look at him. He was having fun! He probably wasn't even sorry he ate my turtle.

That night my father came home with the biggest box of all. It wasn't wrapped up or anything but I knew it was another present. I turned away from my father.

"Peter," he said. "This box is a surprise for you!"

"Well, I don't want another turtle," I said. "Don't think you can make me feel better with another turtle . . . because you can't."

"Who said anything about a turtle, son?" Dad asked. "You see, Peter, your mother and I think you've been a good sport about the whole situation. After all, Dribble *was* your pet."

I looked up. Could I be hearing right? Did they really remember about me and Dribble? I put my hand inside the box. I felt something warm and soft and furry. I knew it was a dog, but I pretended to be surprised when he jumped on my lap and licked me.

Fudge cried, "Ohh . . . doggie! See . . . doggie!" He ran right over and grabbed my dog's tail.

"Fudge," my father said, taking him away. "This is your brother's dog. Maybe someday you'll have a dog of your own. But this one belongs to Peter. Do you understand?"

Fudge nodded. "Peetah's dog."

"That's right," my father said. "Peter's dog!" Then he turned to me. "And just to be sure, son," he said, "we got a dog that's going to grow quite big. *Much* too big for your brother to swallow!"

We all laughed. My dog was neat.

I named him Turtle . . . to remind me.

FEELINGS

by Aliki

I HAVE FEELINGS

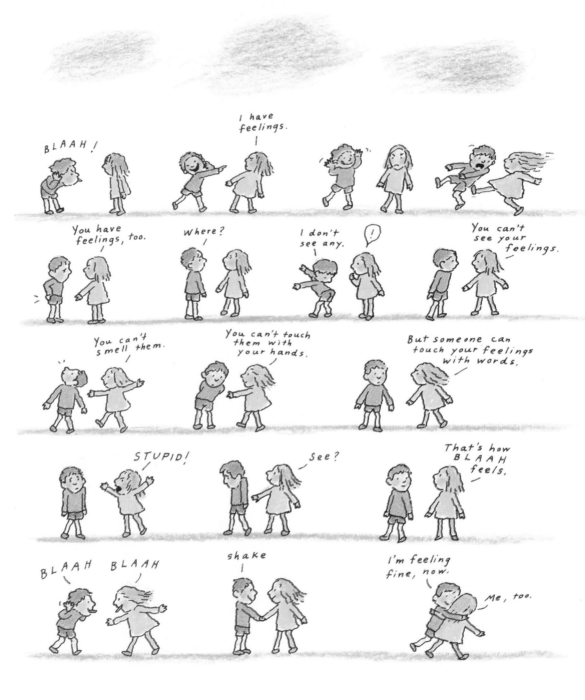

We Have a New Girl in Class

There's nothing to do.
I made my bed.
I practiced my recorder.
I read all my books.
I'm sick of puzzles.
I'm bored,
bored,
BORED.

she sounds
lonely to me.

How Do You Feel?

WHO'S TRAINING WHO?

Most dogs are eager to learn if someone will spend the time to teach them. Here are a few teaching ideas from dog trainer Charles Eisenmann.

"Come on, Rover, come to me!"
    The idea here is first to catch your dog's interest and then match its actions with your command.

    1. Begin teaching this command by taking your dog's favourite toy and walking three steps away.

    2. Hold its toy out in front of you and *as your dog starts to move toward you* call, "Come on, Rover (or whatever your dog's name is), come to me."

    3. When it comes, immediately praise it for doing well and give it a hug. *Don't give it the toy.*

    4. Keep repeating all the steps until you don't need to use the toy any longer. Your dog will come when it's called because it understands that you want it to.

"Sit down, Rover. Please sit down!"

Like all attempts to teach your dog, this one requires patience. Your dog has to learn to hear and remember your command before it can do what you expect of it.

1. Start by standing close to your dog and holding its favourite toy just above its nose. The idea is to make this such an awkward position for it to stand in that it will automatically sit down.

2. *As it starts to sit*, say, "Sit down, Rover. Please sit down." Reward it the instant it sits with words of praise and a hug. *Don't give it the toy*.

3. If your dog backs up rather than sitting down, try again when it has a wall behind it so that it can't move backwards.

4. Repeat all the steps until your dog sits on command.

THE GAMES THAT SEEM

by Red Lane

If there's one thing I like doing
it's playing games
with my friends
or my dog
or even just by myself

And I guess the main reason I like playing
games
is that the games always seem so Real

Like the House game
I play with the girl next door

First we argue who's going to be the father
or the mother
and then we decide to take turns
and our baby is a doll
or sometimes my dog

and we're married

but not Really

And I can even play House by myself
and always be the father

I just pretend I don't have to be married
because I've got my mother
and my sister can be the baby
or my dog can be
and my father can be the Friendly Stranger
who's always going somewhere to do
something
and I just kind of hang around
and look after things

but not Really

because it's just a game I play

Like the Follow The Leader Game
I play with my friends

First we argue who's going to be The Leader
and then we decide because we have to have
a Leader to play
and then we follow The Leader wherever he
goes
and do whatever he does

because we have to

but not Really

And I can even play Follow The Leader by
myself
and always be The Leader
I just pretend that all my friends are
following me
and that they want me to be The Leader
because nobody else is good enough to be
The Leader
and that they follow me wherever I go
because I always go the best way
and that they do whatever I do
because I always do the best things

but not Really

because it's just a game I play

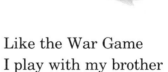

Like the War Game
I play with my brother

First we argue who's going to be the Good
Guy or the Bad Guy
and then we decide we'll both be Good
Guys
and the winner will be the Best Guy
and the loser won't be
because he'll be dead

but not Really

And I can even play War by myself
and always be the Best Guy

I just pretend somebody is my enemy
like my dog
or the next door neighbour
and then I sneak up on them
when they're not watching
and they don't even know they're in the
game
and then shoot them dead

but not Really

because it's just a game I play

But sometimes I wonder
Is it Really a game I play?

What if the Games I play are Really Real!

And then I think
Would I still like to play games
if they are Really Real?

And then I wonder

But I still play games

Do you?

THE BEST CHRISTMAS PAGEANT EVER

by Barbara Robinson

The Herdman children—Ralph, Imogene, Leroy, Claude, Ollie, and Gladys—are the worst kids in town. They decided to take part in the Christmas pageant because they thought there might be free food. They had never heard the Christmas story before, and their interpretation of it has everybody expecting that the pageant will be a disaster.

On the night of the pageant we didn't have any supper because Mother forgot to fix it. My father said that was all right. Between Mrs. Armstrong's telephone calls and the pageant rehearsals, he didn't expect supper anymore.

"When it's all over," he said, "we'll go someplace and have hamburgers." But Mother said when it was all over she might want to go someplace and hide.

"We've never once gone through the whole thing," she said. "I don't know what's going to happen. It may be the first Christmas pageant in history where Joseph and the Wise Men get in a fight, and Mary runs away with the baby."

She might be right, I thought, and I wondered what all of us in the angel choir ought to do in case that happened. It would be dumb for us just to stand there singing about the Holy Infant if Mary had run off with him.

But nothing seemed very different at first.

There was the usual big mess all over the place—baby angels getting poked in the eye by other baby angels' wings and grumpy shepherds stumbling over their bathrobes. The spotlight swooped back and forth and up and down till it made you sick at your stomach to look at it and, as usual, whoever was playing the piano pitched "Away in a Manger" so high we could hardly hear it, let alone sing it. My father says "Away in a Manger" always starts out sounding like a closetful of mice.

But everything settled down, and at 7:30 the pageant began.

While we sang "Away in a Manger," the ushers lit candles all around the church, and the spotlight came on to be the star. So you really had to know the words to "Away in a Manger" because you couldn't see anything—not even Alice Wendleken's vaseline eyelids.

After that we sang two verses of "O, Little Town of Bethlehem," and then we were supposed to hum some more "O, Little Town of Bethlehem" while Mary and Joseph came in from a side door. Only they didn't come right away. So we hummed and hummed and hummed, which is boring and also very hard, and before long doesn't sound like any song at all—more like an old refrigerator.

"I knew something like this would happen," Alice Wendleken whispered to me. "They didn't come at all! We won't have any Mary and Joseph—and now what are we supposed to do?"

I guess we would have gone on humming till we all turned blue, but we didn't have to. Ralph and Imogene were there all right, only for once they didn't come through the door pushing each other out of the way. They just stood there for a minute as if they weren't sure they were in the right place—because of the candles, I guess, and the church being full of people. They looked like the people you see on the six o'clock news—refugees, sent to wait in some strange ugly place, with all their boxes and sacks around them.

It suddenly occurred to me that this was just the way it must have been for the real Holy Family, stuck away in a barn by people who didn't much care what happened to them. They couldn't have been very neat and tidy either, but more like *this* Mary and Joseph (Imogene's veil was cockeyed as usual, and Ralph's hair stuck out all around his ears). Imogene had the baby doll but she wasn't carrying it the way she was supposed to, cradled in her arms. She had it slung up over her shoulder, and before she put it in the manger she thumped it twice on the back.

I heard Alice gasp and she poked me. "I don't think it's very nice to burp the baby Jesus," she whispered, "as if he had colic." Then she poked me again. "Do you suppose he could have had colic?"

I said, "I don't know why not," and I didn't. He *could* have had

colic, or been fussy, or hungry like any other baby. After all, that was the whole point of Jesus—that he didn't come down on a cloud like something out of "Amazing Comics," but that he was born and lived . . . a real person.

Right away we had to sing "While Shepherds Watched Their Flocks by Night"—and we had to sing very loud, because there were more shepherds than there were anything else, and they made so much noise, banging their crooks around like a lot of hockey sticks.

Next came Gladys, from behind the angel choir, pushing people out of the way and stepping on everyone's feet. Since Gladys was the only one in the pageant who had anything to say she made the most of it: "Hey! Unto you a child is born!" she hollered, as if it was, for sure, the best news in the world. And all the shepherds trembled, sore afraid—of Gladys, mainly, but it looked good anyway.

Then came three carols about angels. It took that long to get the angels in because they were all primary kids and they got nervous and cried and forgot where they were supposed to go and bent their wings in the door and things like that.

We got a little rest then, while the boys sang "We Three Kings of Orient Are," and everybody in the audience shifted around to watch the Wise Men march up the aisle.

"What have they got?" Alice whispered.

I didn't know, but whatever it was, it was heavy—Leroy almost dropped it. He didn't have his frankincense jar either, and Claude and Ollie didn't have anything although they were supposed to bring the gold and the myrrh.

"I knew this would happen," Alice said for the second time. "I bet it's something awful."

"Like what?"

"Like . . . a burnt offering. You know the Herdmans."

Well, they did burn things, but they hadn't burned this yet. It was a ham—and right away I knew where it came from. My father was on the church charitable works committee—they give away food baskets at Christmas, and this was the Herdman's food-basket ham. It still had the ribbon around it, saying Merry Christmas.

"I'll bet they stole that!" Alice said.

"They did not. It came from their food basket, and if they want to give away their own ham I guess they can do it." But even if the Herdmans didn't *like* ham (that was Alice's next idea) they had never before in their lives given anything away except lumps on the head. So you had to be impressed.

Leroy dropped the ham in front of the manger. It looked funny to see a ham there instead of the fancy bath-salts jars we always used for the myrrh and the frankincense. And then they went and sat down in the only space that was left.

While we sang "What Child Is This?" the Wise Men were supposed to confer among themselves and then leave by a different door, so everyone would understand that they were going home another way. But the Herdmans forgot, or didn't want to, or something, because they didn't confer and they didn't leave either. They just sat there, and there wasn't anything anyone could do about it.

"They're ruining the whole thing!" Alice whispered, but they weren't at all. As a matter of fact, it made perfect sense for the Wise Men to sit down and rest, and I said so.

"They're supposed to have come a long way. You wouldn't expect them just to show up, hand over the ham, and leave!"

As for ruining the whole thing, it seemed to me that the Herdmans had improved the pageant a lot, just by doing what came naturally—like burping the baby, for instance, or thinking a ham would make a better present than a lot of perfumed oil.

Usually, by the time we got to "Silent Night," which was always the last carol, I was fed up with the whole thing and couldn't wait for it to be over. But I didn't feel that way this time. I almost wished for the pageant to go on, with the Herdmans in charge, to see what else they would do that was different.

Maybe the Wise Men would tell Mary about their problem with Herod, and she would tell them to go back and lie their heads off.

Or Joseph might go with them and get rid of Herod once and for all. Or Joseph and Mary might ask the Wise Men to take the Christ Child with them, figuring that no one would think to look there.

I was so busy planning new ways to save the baby Jesus that I missed the beginning of "Silent Night," but it was all right because everyone sang "Silent Night," including the audience. We sang all the verses too, and when we got to "Son of God, Love's pure light" I happened to look at Imogene and I almost dropped my hymn book on a baby angel.

Everyone had been waiting all this time for the Herdmans to do something absolutely unexpected. And sure enough, that was what happened.

Imogene Herdman was crying.

In the candlelight her face was all shiny with tears and she didn't even bother to wipe them away. She just sat there—awful old Imogene—in her crookedy veil, crying and crying and crying.

Well. It *was* the best Christmas pageant we ever had.

Everybody said so, but nobody seemed to know why. When it was over people stood around the lobby of the church talking about what was different this year. There was something special, everyone said—they couldn't put their finger on what.

Mrs. Wendleken said, "Well, Mary the mother of Jesus had a black eye; that was something special. But only what you might expect," she added.

She meant that it was the most natural thing in the world for a Herdman to have a black eye. But actually nobody hit Imogene and she didn't hit anyone else. Her eye wasn't really black either, just all puffy and swollen. She had walked into the corner of the choir-robe cabinet, in a kind of daze—as if she had just caught onto the idea of God, and the wonder of Christmas.

And this was the funny thing about it all. For years, I'd thought about the wonder of Christmas, and the mystery of Jesus' birth, and never really understood it. But now, because of the Herdmans, it didn't seem so mysterious after all.

When Imogene had asked me what the pageant was about, I

told her it was about Jesus, but that was just part of it. It was about a new baby, and his mother and father who were in a lot of trouble—no money, no place to go, no doctor, nobody they knew. And then, arriving from the East (like my uncle from New Jersey) some rich friends.

But Imogene, I guess, didn't see it that way. Christmas just came over her all at once, like a case of chills and fever. And so she was crying, and walking into the furniture.

Afterward there were candy canes and little tiny Testaments for everyone, and a poinsettia plant for my mother from the whole Sunday school. We put the costumes away and folded up the collapsible manger, and just before we left, my father snuffed out the last of the tall white candles.

"I guess that's everything," he said as we stood at the back of the church. "All over now. It was quite a pageant." Then he looked at my mother. "What's that you've got?"

"It's the ham," she said. "They wouldn't take it back. They wouldn't take any candy either, or any of the little Bibles. But Imogene did ask me for a set of the Bible-story pictures, and she took out the Mary picture and said it was exactly right, whatever that means."

I think it meant that no matter how she herself was, Imogene liked the idea of the Mary in the picture—all pink and white and pure-looking, as if she never washed the dishes or cooked supper or did anything at all except have Jesus on Christmas Eve.

But as far as I'm concerned, Mary is always going to look a lot like Imogene Herdman—sort of nervous and bewildered, but ready to clobber anyone who laid a hand on her baby. And the Wise Men are always going to be Leroy and his brothers, bearing ham.

When we came out of the church that night it was cold and clear, with crunchy snow underfoot and bright, bright stars overhead. And I thought about the Angel of the Lord—Gladys, with her skinny legs and her dirty sneakers sticking out from under her robe, yelling at all of us, everywhere:

"Hey! Unto you a child is born!"

MY FAVOURITE THINGS

by Oscar Hammerstein II

Raindrops on roses and whiskers on kittens,
Bright copper kettles and warm woollen mittens,
Brown paper packages tied up with strings,
These are a few of my favourite things.

Cream coloured ponies and crisp apple strudels,
Doorbells and sleighbells and schnitzel with noodles,
Wild geese that fly with the moon on their wings,
These are a few of my favourite things.

When the dog bites,
When the bee stings,
When I'm feeling sad,
I simply remember my favourite things
And then I don't feel so bad.

Girls in white dresses with blue satin sashes,
Snowflakes that stay on my nose and eyelashes,
Silver white winters that melt into springs,
These are a few of my favourite things.

PLAYGROUND RHYMES

Humpty Dumpty sat on a wall
Eating black bananas
Where do you think he put the skins?
Down the king's pyjamas.

Inky pinky ponky
Daddy bought a donkey
Donkey died, Daddy cried
Inky pinky ponky

Skinny Malink melodeon legs
Big banana feet
Went to the pictures
And couldn't find a seat
When he found a seat
He fell half asleep
Skinny Malink melodeon legs
Big banana feet

Are you the guy
    That told the guy
    That I'm the guy
    That gave the guy
    The black eye

No I'm not the guy
That told the guy
That you're the guy
That gave the guy
The black eye

Granny's in the kitchen
Doing a bit of stitching
In came a bogeyman
And chased granny out

"Well" says granny
"That's not fair"
"Well" says the bogeyman
"I don't care"

She stood on the bridge at midnight
Her lips were all aquiver
She gave a cough
Her leg fell off
And floated down the river

Ladies and Jellyspoons
I come before you
To stand behind you
And tell you something
I know nothing about
Next Thursday
Which is Good Friday
There'll be a Mother's Meeting
For Fathers only
Wear your best clothes if you haven't any
And if you can come
Please stay at home
Admission free
Pay at the door
Take a seat
And sit on the floor
It makes no difference where you sit
The man in the gallery is sure to spit

ON FOUR PAWS

For many people, pets are important members of the family. Since the time of cave dwellers, humans have tried to tame creatures of the wild to live with us—as guards, as workers, and as company. After all, humans are animals, too, and need to bring nature into their lives.

Some people try to keep wild animals as pets and meet many difficulties, because it can take generations for an animal to become domesticated. Do you think the creature in the following excerpt should be a pet?

> *Mark sat down in the sun-drenched doorway and began opening the paper bag. "I saved one of my sandwiches for you, and a couple of the kids didn't eat all theirs so I brought them along too."*
>
> *Ben tried to get his big black nose into the sack, and Mark pushed it away. He hit the back of Ben's front legs just above his feet and said "Down! Sit down, Ben." He patted the floor beside him. Ben stretched out, big forepaws extended. Mark didn't know*

how he had taught Ben that, or even if he had. But Ben always lay down when Mark did it.

Mark tore the sandwiches into chunks and held them in his palm. Ben lifted the pieces so deftly Mark scarcely felt his tongue. The bear ate them with a great smacking of lips. When it was all gone, Ben pushed at his hand, looking for more. Mark gave him the empty sack, and Ben ripped it apart, snorting and huffing at the aroma that remained. When he was satisfied there was no more, he dropped his big head on his forepaws and lay looking out at the bright spring day.

(from *Gentle Ben*, by Walt Morey)

The boy and the bear seem to be friends, but can a bear ever forget he is a creature of the wild?

In the selections in this section, you will read about different kinds of animals. Some are pets, some are free, and others are caught halfway between two worlds. You will also read about the world humans and animals share—about what life is like "on four paws."

RIKKI-TIKKI-TAVI

by Rudyard Kipling

Teddy found Rikki-tikki-tavi in a ditch one summer morning after a heavy rain. The rising water had washed the little mongoose from its burrow, and Teddy had carried it home inside his shirt. Teddy and his father and his mother were English. They were living in India where Teddy's father was doing business for the King. Teddy begged to keep the little mongoose for a pet, but Teddy's mother was fearful about having a mongoose in the house. When Teddy's father came home that evening, he reassured his wife that a mongoose would be good protection against the danger of snakes in the garden, and so Teddy was given permission to keep the homeless little mongoose.

Every morning after his breakfast of bits of banana and boiled egg, Rikki-tikki-tavi scuttled around the bushes in the garden just to see what was to be seen. He was rather like a little cat in his fur and tail, but quite like a weasel in his head and habits. His eyes and the end of his restless nose were pink; he could scratch himself anywhere he pleased with any leg, front or back; he could fluff up his tail till it looked like a bottle-brush; and his war cry as he scuttled through the long grass was: *Rikk-tikk-tikki-tikki-tchk!*

One morning when Rikki-tikki-tavi was in the garden, he heard Darzee, the tailor-bird, sitting on her nest in the pine tree, crying. A tailor-bird looks and sounds something like a cat-bird. Rikki-tikki stood up on his hind legs and asked: "What's the matter with you?"

"Oh, Rikki, a terrible thing happened. One of my babies fell out of the nest yesterday and Nag ate him."

"Hm-m!" said Rikki-tikki, "That is very sad—but I am a stranger here. Who is Nag?"

Just then the little mongoose heard a cold, horrid sound behind him that made him jump two feet into the air and whirl around. Inch by inch out of the grass rose up the head and spread hood of Nag, the black king cobra, who was five feet long from tongue to tail.

When he had lifted one third of himself clear of the ground, he stayed balancing to and fro exactly as a dandelion tuft balances in the wind, and he looked at Rikki-tikki with wicked eyes that never changed expression, whatever the snake might have been thinking.

"Who is Nag?" he said. "I am Nag. Look, and be afraid!"

It is true that Rikki-tikki was afraid for a moment; but it was impossible for him to stay frightened for any length of time.

Though Rikki had never met a live cobra before, his mother had fed him on dead ones, and he knew that a grown mongoose's business in life was to fight and eat snakes. Nag knew that, too, and at the bottom of his cold heart, he, too, was afraid.

Suddenly Darzee, the tailor-bird, who was sitting on her nest in the pine tree watching the two below, cried out: "Behind you, Rikki! Look behind you!"

Fortunately Rikki-tikki knew better than to waste time in looking. He jumped up into the air as high as he could go, and just under him whizzed the black blur of another snake.

It was another cobra, Nagaina, Nag's wicked mate. She had crept up behind Rikki as he was talking to make an end of him; and he heard her savage hiss as the stroke missed. Rikki-tikki came down almost across her back. If he had been a wise, full-grown mongoose, he would have known that then was the time to scramble up the snake's back and to break her neck by biting sharply just above her spread hood. He bit, indeed, in the middle of her back where it did little damage. Then he jumped clear of the snake to avoid the terrible lashing return-stroke of the cobra, which sometimes can be just as deadly to a mongoose as the cobra's bite. Nagaina was left torn and angry.

Now it is said that when a cobra misses its stroke, it never says anything or gives any sign of what it means to do next. Without a word Nagaina slithered off through the tall grass to reconnoitre, and Nag followed her.

That night Teddy carried Rikki-tikki off to bed with him. Rikki-tikki was too well bred to bite or scratch, but as soon as Teddy was asleep, he went off for his night walk around the house.

Instantly Rikki-tikki knew that something was strange about this night. The house was as still as still, but he thought he could hear the faintest scratch-scratch in the world, a noise as faint as that of a fly walking on a windowpane. He listened. Then he recognized the sound as that of snake scales scratching on brickwork. He knew immediately that it was Nag or Nagaina trying to enter the house. But where?

He remembered a loose brick at the back of the bathroom; the brick could be pulled out to drain the bath water from the tub to the creek near the house. Plumbing facilities in India are not always the same as ours. Rikki-tikki crept down the dark hall and turned into the bathroom.

Pressing his lithe body against the plastered wall, he listened and heard Nag and Nagaina whispering together outside in the moonlight. Nag was saying, "You go back to our nest in the melon patch at the back of the garden, Nagaina. Take care of our eggs. They have been left alone too long. I will creep into the bathroom and wait until the master comes in for his bath in the morning. Then I'll kill him and his wife and his child. When the family is

dead, the bungalow will be empty, and Rikki-tikki will leave here. And once again the garden will belong to us."

Rikki-tikki heard Nagaina slither off toward the melon patch at the back of the garden. Then he saw, or thought he saw, the black beady eyes of the cobra as Nag pushed his head around the loose brick and pulled the cold five feet of his body into the room after him. Rikki-tikki heard the cobra rise up and lap water from the water jar. Then he heard the cobra wrap himself, coil by coil, around the bulge at the bottom of the water jar.

After an hour Rikki-tikki began to move, muscle by muscle, towards the jar. Nag was asleep, and Rikki-tikki looked at his big back, wondering which would be the best place for a good hold.

"If I don't break his back at the first jump," said Rikki, "he can still fight; and if he fights—O Rikki!" He looked at the thickness of the neck below the hood, but that was too much for him; and a bite near the tail would only make Nag savage. "It must be the head," he said at last. "The head above the hood; and, when I am once there, I must not let go."

Then he jumped and sank his teeth deep into Nag's head which was lying a little clear of the water jar. It only took Nag a moment to uncoil. Then he battered Rikki-tikki to and fro, as a rat is shaken by a dog, to and fro on the floor, up and down, and around in great circles. Rikki-tikki thought he would surely be killed in the encounter, but he was certain of one thing: when the family found him, he would still be clinging to the snake's head.

Then Rikki-tikki saw a ball of fire shoot past him, and he felt its hot breath . . . When he regained consciousness, Teddy was holding the little mongoose in his arms, showering him with praise and affection. He was saying that Rikki-tikki had saved the family. Teddy's father had been awakened by the fight in the bathroom, and he had fired two shots into the cobra's hood. Nag, the black king cobra, was dead.

Without waiting for breakfast, Rikki-tikki escaped to the veranda and nursed his tired and bruised body in the warm sunshine. He stretched out on the brickwork and was almost asleep when he

heard Darzee singing, "Nag is dead—is dead—is dead!"

The news of Nag's death was all over the garden, and the frogs and birds joined in the chorus, "Nag is dead—is dead—is dead!"

"Yes," said Darzee. "The maid has thrown Nag's lifeless body out on the rubbish heap. Nag will never eat my babies again."

"Oh, you stupid tuft of feathers," said Rikki angrily. "Is this the time to sing? Where is Nagaina?"

"Nag is dead—is dead—is dead!" Darzee went on, singing at the top of her voice. "The valiant Rikki-tikki caught Nag by the head and held fast. The big man brought the bang-stick, and Nag fell in two pieces."

"Stop singing a minute, Darzee," said Rikki. "Where is Nagaina?"

"What is it, O Killer of the terrible Nag?"asked Darzee.

"Where is Nagaina?"

"On the rubbish heap by the stables, mourning for Nag. Great is Rikki-tikki with the white teeth."

"Bother my white teeth! Have you ever heard where she keeps her eggs?"

"In the melon bed, on the end nearest the wall, where the sun strikes nearly all day," said Darzee. "She hid them there three weeks ago."

Rikki-tikki turned and fled down the garden path, past the stable and the tool shed, on to the melon patch near the wall. There, underneath the melon leaves, he found Nagaina's nest very cunningly concealed. In it were twenty-six cobra eggs.

A cobra's nest is nothing more than a hole scooped out in the soft earth. The cobra eggs looked not unlike the eggs that we keep in our refrigerator at home, except that the cobra eggs were encased in a soft, white, transparent skin instead of in a hard shell. Inside of each egg Rikki-tikki could see a baby cobra curled up, and he knew that the eggs would hatch within the day.

The little mongoose chuckled to himself as he clipped the end of the first egg and killed the little snake within it. He remembered that his mother had told him that a baby cobra can kill a man or a mongoose. Methodically, Rikki-tikki fished egg after egg from the nest and destroyed them. All the while he was keeping a sharp watch lest Nagaina should return. At last there was but one egg left.

As Rikki-tikki pulled it from the nest, Darzee, the tailor-bird, flew to him from her nest in the pine tree, screaming, "Rikki-tikki! Come! Come! Nagaina has gone onto the veranda! Oh, come quickly! She means killing!"

Rikki-tikki grasped the last egg in his mouth and scuttled up the garden path as hard as he could put foot to ground. He bounded up the veranda steps two at a time.

What he saw caused him to stop so short that he skidded halfway across the brickwork. Teddy, his father and mother were seated there at early breakfast, but Rikki-tikki saw that they were not eating. They sat stone-still, and their faces were white.

Coiled at the foot of Teddy's chair within easy striking distance of Teddy's bare leg was Nagaina. She was swaying to and fro, singing a song of triumph.

"Son of the big man that killed Nag!" she hissed. "Wait a little. Keep very still, all you three! If you move I strike, and if you do not

move I strike. Oh, foolish people who killed my Nag!"

Teddy's eyes were fixed on his father, and all his father could do was to whisper, "Sit still, Teddy. You mustn't move. Teddy, you mustn't move."

Rikki-tikki bounded out onto the veranda behind Nagaina and spit the last egg from his mouth. "Turn around, Nagaina. Turn and fight! Look at the last of your eggs. I found your nest in the melon patch and destroyed all of the eggs but this one."

Nagaina spun clear round, forgetting everything for the sake of her one egg. At the same moment Teddy's father shot out a big hand, caught Teddy by the shoulder, and dragged him across the table, spilling the dishes and the food to the floor with a clatter.

"Tricked! Tricked! *Rikkk-tck-tck!*" chuckled Rikki-tikki. "The boy is safe now, and it was I—I—I that caught Nag by the hood last night in the bathroom." The little mongoose began to jump up and down, all four feet together, his head close to the floor. "Nag threw me to and fro, but he couldn't shake me off. He was dead before the big man blew him in two. I did it! *Rikki-tikki-tck-tck!* Come, then,

Nagaina. Come and fight with me. You shall not be a widow long."

Now the family drew back against the porch railing, watching the battle of life and death that was taking place before them. Nagaina was striking again and again. After each strike she would recoil as quickly as a watch-spring, ready to strike again.

Rikki-tikki was bounding all around Nagaina, keeping just out of reach of her stroke. His little pink eyes had turned red, like hot coals. He was standing up on his hind feet like a little kangaroo, ready to spring at the snake's neck whenever he found the opening. All the while he was sounding his battle cry, *"Rikki-tikki-tck-tck!"*

Again and again and again she struck. Each time her head came with a whack on the brickwork of the veranda, she gathered herself together to strike again.

Rikki-tikki danced in a circle to get behind her, and Nagaina spun round to keep her head to his head. Rikki had forgotten the egg. He had moved so far from it, that Nagaina came nearer and nearer to it. At last, she caught the egg in her mouth, turned to the veranda steps, and flew like an arrow down the path—with Rikki-tikki right behind.

It is said that when the cobra runs for its life, it goes like the whiplash flicked across the horse's neck. But Rikki-tikki was even faster. He caught Nagaina by the tail as she plunged into the rat hole where she and Nag used to live. Rikki-tikki tried to pull her back, but Nagaina was the stronger of the two, and inch by inch, she pulled the little mongoose into the hole with her.

And Darzee, the tailor-bird, who was sitting in the pine tree watching the battle taking place below, set up a very mournful chant: "It's all over with Rikki-tikki-tavi! Brave Rikki-tikki-tavi! Even a wise, full-grown mongoose would not follow a cobra into its own hole."

Presently the grass that grew around the rat hole quivered, and Rikki-tikki-tavi, covered with dirt, dragged himself out of the hole leg by leg. He stopped to shake the dust from his whiskers; then he looked up at Darzee, the tailor-bird, and said: "It's all over. Nagaina is dead."

And the red ants that lived between the grass stems heard him and began trooping down one after another to see if what Rikki-tikki-tavi had said was true.

And as for Rikki-tikki-tavi, he lay down in the sunshine beside the rat hole and went to sleep. He slept all of that morning and half of the afternoon, because for a little mongoose he had done a hard day's work.

YOUR OWN BEST SECRET PLACE

by Byrd Baylor

His name is
William Cottonwood.

That's all
I know about him . . .
just that
and
the way
he loved
a secret place
he had to
leave.

I think of
William Cottonwood
a lot.

I wish I knew
where
he is
now.

I'd tell him
how
I found
his secret place
and how
I'm
taking care of it
and that
I hope
he doesn't mind
my being there.

Or
you
could tell him
for me.

If you ever meet
somebody
and his name is

William Cottonwood
and he used to live
by the Rio Grande River
in a valley
in New Mexico where
there are
chili farms
and cornfields . . .
then
ask him
if
he left
three messages
nailed up
on a hollow tree.

If he says yes,
then he's
the William Cottonwood
I'm looking for.

Tell him
this
for me.

Just say
I found this place
by accident.

I noticed
a hollow
in the foot of
a cottonwood tree.

Then
I was down
on my hands and knees
looking in,
expecting to see—
maybe fox tracks.

But what I saw was
a ragged
blue blanket
back there
in the hole
and
next to the blanket
a red coffee can.

I thought I shouldn't
go inside
since
someone else's
things
were
there.

I started to
leave.

That's when I saw
three notes
nailed up
on the tree.

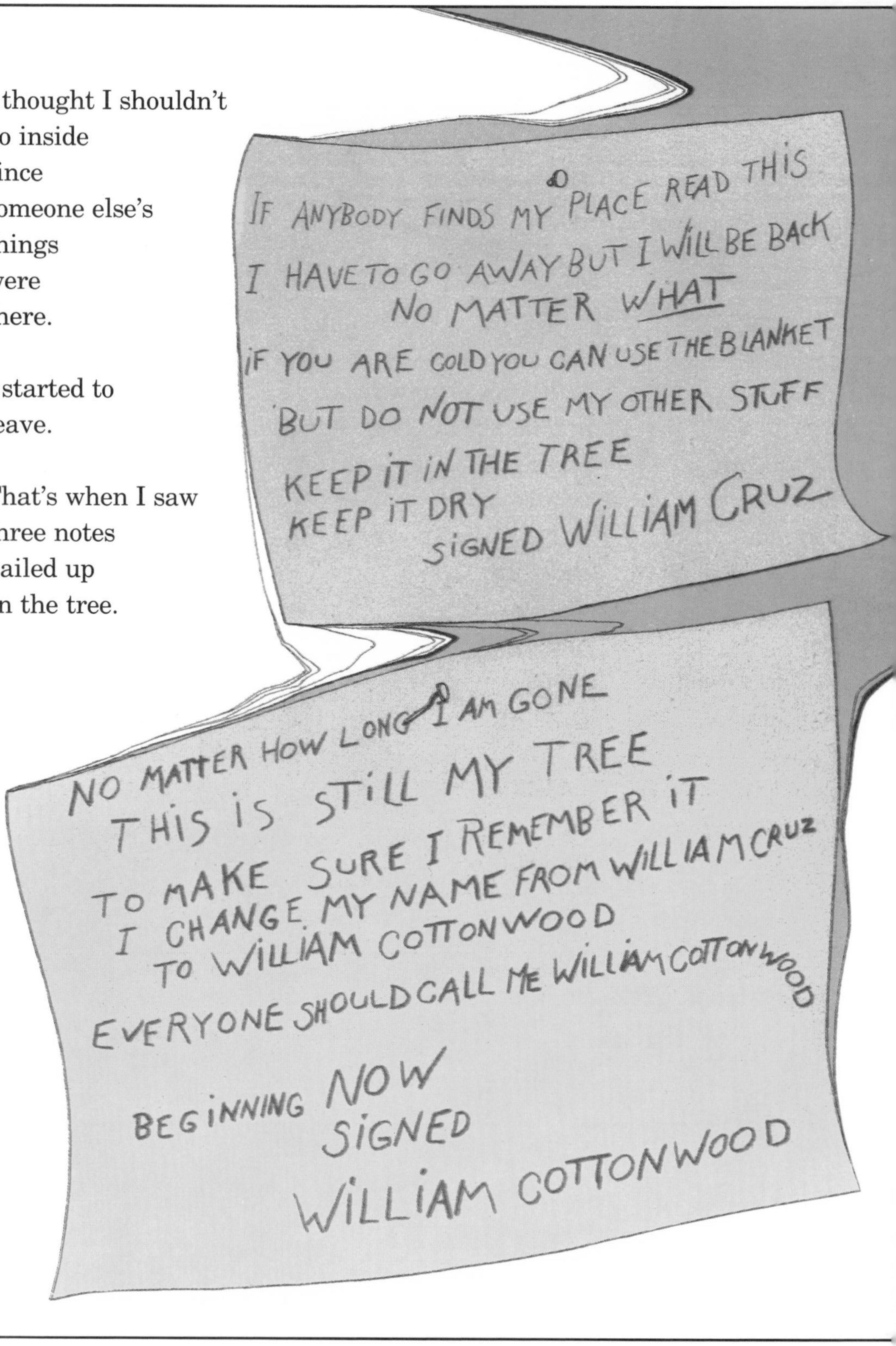

IF ANYBODY FINDS MY PLACE READ THIS
I HAVE TO GO AWAY BUT I WILL BE BACK
NO MATTER WHAT
IF YOU ARE COLD YOU CAN USE THE BLANKET
BUT DO NOT USE MY OTHER STUFF
KEEP IT IN THE TREE
KEEP IT DRY
SIGNED WILLIAM CRUZ

NO MATTER HOW LONG I AM GONE
THIS IS STILL MY TREE
TO MAKE SURE I REMEMBER IT
I CHANGE MY NAME FROM WILLIAM CRUZ
TO WILLIAM COTTONWOOD
EVERYONE SHOULD CALL ME WILLIAM COTTONWOOD
BEGINNING NOW
SIGNED
WILLIAM COTTONWOOD

You could tell
they were written
on brown paper sacks
he had cut
into squares.

GOODBY
SIGNED
WILLIAM COTTONWOOD

I stayed
where I was,
curled up like a
fox,
cozy
and warm,
looking out
at the rain.

I began
to understand
how
William Cottonwood
felt there.

Then
it seemed like we
were
friends
and maybe
he'd want me
to look
at the things
he had left
in that red
coffee can—

so I did.

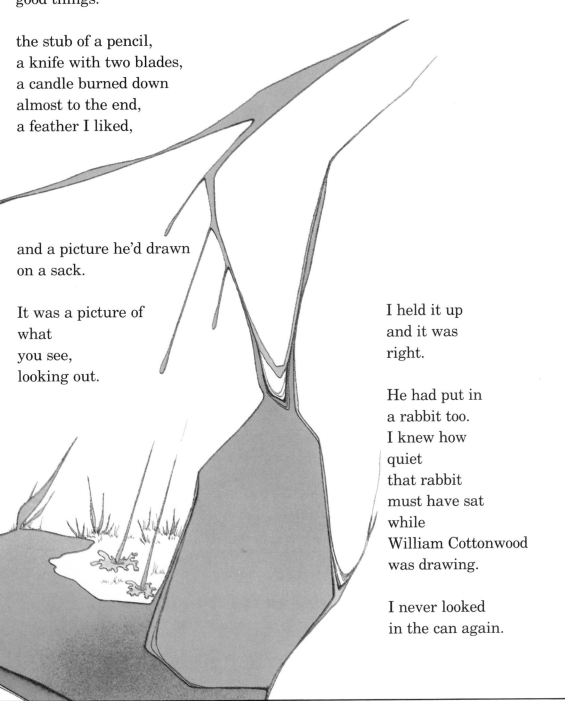

They were all
good things:

the stub of a pencil,
a knife with two blades,
a candle burned down
almost to the end,
a feather I liked,

and a picture he'd drawn
on a sack.

It was a picture of
what
you see,
looking out.

I held it up
and it was
right.

He had put in
a rabbit too.
I knew how
quiet
that rabbit
must have sat
while
William Cottonwood
was drawing.

I never looked
in the can again.

If you find him
and you take him
to your own
best
secret
place,
then
while you're
sitting there
together

just tell him this
for me.

Say
I keep a list
of all the
birds
and animals
I see
from where I sit
inside his tree,
looking out.

Say I've brought
another
coffee can.
I keep the list
in it.
It's there
for him to read
when he
comes home.

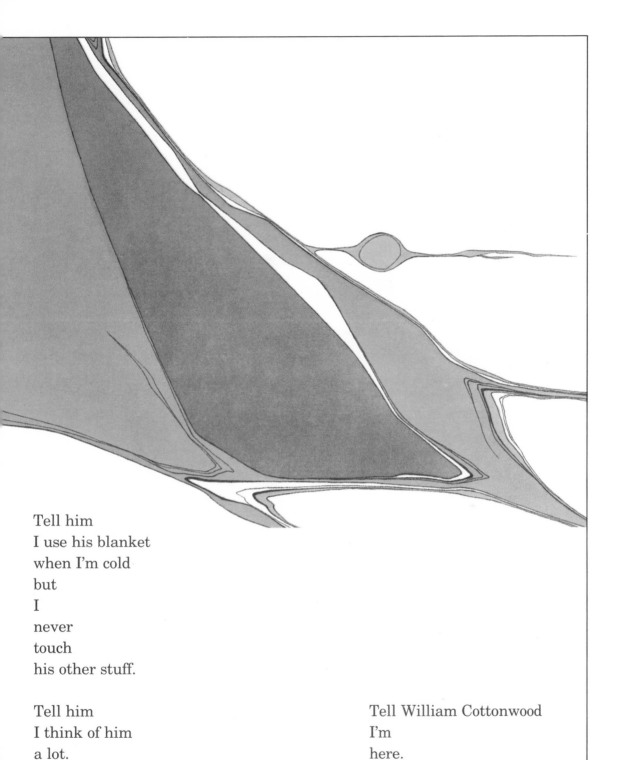

Tell him
I use his blanket
when I'm cold
but
I
never
touch
his other stuff.

Tell him
I think of him
a lot.

Tell William Cottonwood
I'm
here.

POEMS OF THE FIELD

by Joanne Ryder

Frog waits
near the shore,
watching.
He breathes
The water ripples.
He waits.

A shiny fly
buzzes
over the ripples.
Below,
fish stops
waiting
and leaps
high—
surprising
the fly,
surprising
frog.

Fox
forgets
the tree trunk
isn't empty

Downwind
everybody knows
skunk is angry.

The meadow hides secrets
in its deepest places.
Under the sky
under the grass
under the moles
under the rock
dinosaurs sleep.

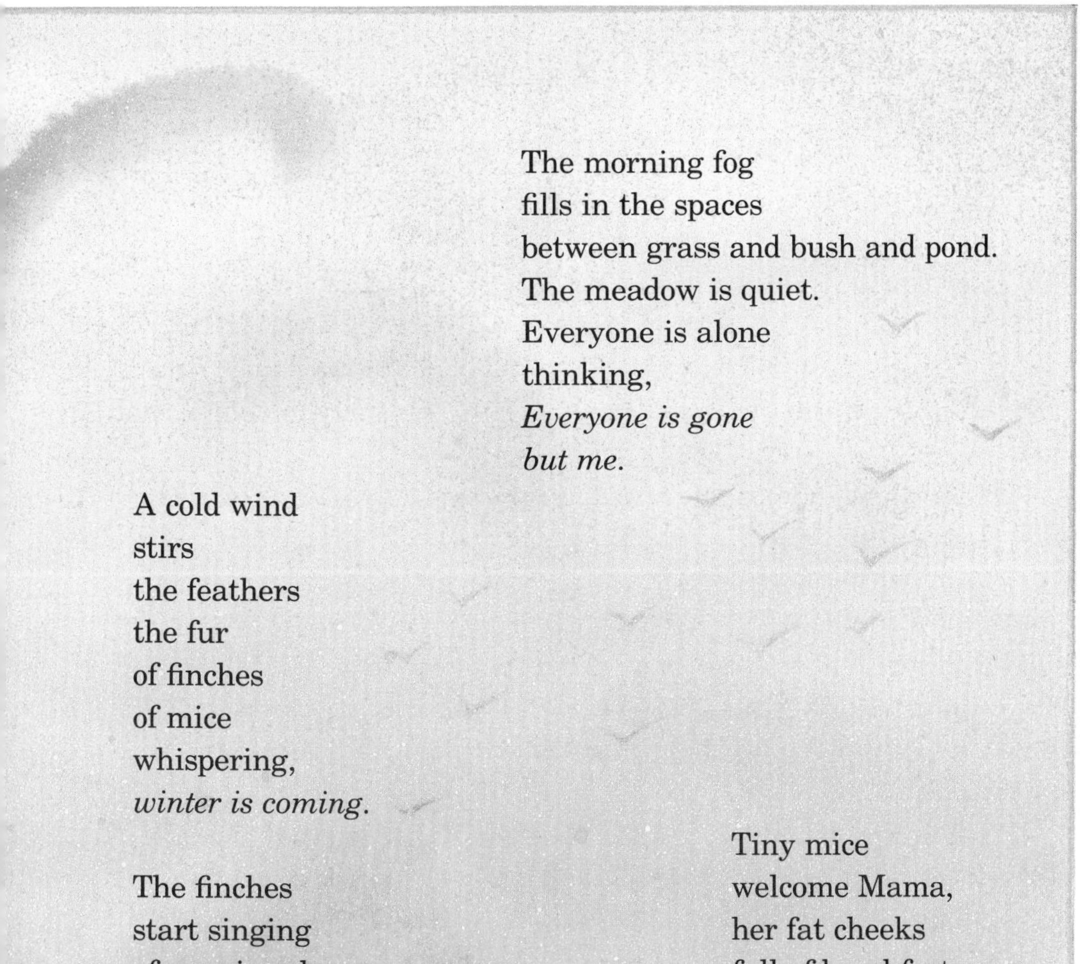

The morning fog
fills in the spaces
between grass and bush and pond.
The meadow is quiet.
Everyone is alone
thinking,
*Everyone is gone
but me.*

A cold wind
stirs
the feathers
the fur
of finches
of mice
whispering,
winter is coming.

The finches
start singing
of sunnier places
but the mice—
making warm nests
underground—
do not hear them.

Tiny mice
welcome Mama,
her fat cheeks
full of breakfast.

THE STARE OF THE CAT

by Eiko Takeda

Long ago in a village in the mountains of Japan there was a small stray cat called Mi-ko. One New Year's day it was bitterly cold and snowing hard. All the villagers huddled round their fires thankful to be warm and safe at home. Only Mi-ko had no home to go to.

From house to house he trudged mewing sadly. But door after door stayed firmly shut.

"I can't go on much longer," thought the little cat as he reached the end of the village.

In the very last house there lived an old couple. All day they had been celebrating the New Year with prayers and offerings to the gods. They were preparing to go to bed when they heard a faint cry outside.

"Who could be out on a night like this?" said the old woman. She ran to the door and peered out. There was Mi-ko shivering on the pathway.

"Come in, come in!" cried the old woman and she carried him gently in to her husband.

"See what the New Year has brought us," she said.

"Perhaps the gods sent him to look after us in our old age," said the husband. He took Mi-ko on his knee and warmed him by the fire. The old woman hurriedly prepared tasty rice cakes for him to eat. Mi-ko began to purr.

"I shall be happy living here," he thought.

So time passed until spring came. This was a busy season for the old couple because they were silkworm farmers. They kept thousands of tiny silkworms which grew, like caterpillars, until they were big enough to spin cocoons, beautiful cocoons of fine silk thread.

Silkworms like to eat mulberry leaves and the more they eat the faster they grow. So all day long, the old couple had to collect mulberry leaves and feed the worms. And day and night the worms

ate on: Rustle! munch! rustle! scrunch!

But late at night when the old couple had gone to bed the rats came out of their holes and down from the rafters. Scuttle scuttle scuttle, they ran onto the tables and began to gobble the worms. Mi-ko watched horrified. If all the worms were eaten there would be no cocoons, and no fine silk thread. The rats had to be stopped. Mi-ko took a deep breath and threw himself towards them.

"Stupid little cat!" screamed the rats. "How dare you try to scare us! Look at him trying to be ferocious, pretending he is the Great Mountain Cat. We'll teach him not to play games!"

They turned on him with their sharp teeth, hundreds of rats, attacking on all sides. Then, leaving him lying bitten and bleeding, they finished their meal of silkworms.

In the morning half the worms were gone. The old couple were sad and worried. "I have failed them," thought Mi-ko. "I must learn how to scare those rats!" But what was it the rats had said? Something about the Great Mountain Cat. "Perhaps he can help me," thought Mi-ko. "I will find him and ask him to teach me."

He set off at once and by nightfall had reached the Great Mountain. Up and up he climbed. The mountain got steeper and steeper, the trees got thicker and thicker, the night got darker and darker. Then suddenly the trees began to shake and the ground trembled and a roaring voice echoed all around.

"GRRROW! What are you doing on MY mountain?"

Mi-ko shook with fear, but stood his ground.

"Great Mountain Cat," he whispered, "I beg you to teach me your terrible art. I must learn to scare away the rats that steal the silkworms every spring."

Two huge eyes appeared out of the darkness.

"The secret lies in my fearsome stare," roared the Great Mountain Cat. "Little Mi-ko, are you not afraid to learn?"

"Yes, but I must," said Mi-ko.

"Then learn to stare steadily, endlessly," snarled the Cat, and as he spoke flames spurted out of his mouth. The trees, the ground, and even the rocks caught fire and began to blaze.

"Stare straight at this fire," roared the Great Mountain Cat. "Do not look away for an instant."

The fire grew fiercer and fiercer. Mi-ko's fur began to sizzle and burn. He almost staggered back but he remembered the rats. Digging his claws into the ground he stared into the heart of the fire. Day after day, night after night, the fire kept burning and burning, hotter and hotter and hotter. And Mi-ko stared steadily into it. And slowly spring and summer passed without him even noticing.

"Not bad, little Mi-ko," the Great Mountain Cat said, at last. "But that is not all there is to learn. Now you must widen your stare and learn to look everywhere all at once."

As he spoke he spat out flames in every direction. Fires sprang up all around until the whole mountain seemed alight. "Now look at all these fires at once," cried the Great Mountain Cat.

"My eyes are melting," moaned Mi-ko. Tears streamed down his nose and sizzled away. But he would not give up. In every direction the fires blazed, and Mi-ko stared at them all. And slowly his eyes grew bigger and stronger until they were huge and glaring balls of light.

So the autumn passed and the winter too. And still Mi-ko stared unblinking. Until at last the Great Mountain Cat spoke once again.

"Enough! Little Mi-ko, you have learned enough!" The flames flickered and died. And Mi-ko found himself face to face with the Great Mountain Cat.

"Well done, little cat," he said.

Feeling a little dazed, Mi-ko set off for home. Around him the flowers bloomed and birds sang. Spring had returned again. The couple were delighted to see him.

"We thought you had gone forever," they said. "Where have you been? And how you've changed! You seem older now, and stronger." Mi-ko purred happily.

"Just wait until tonight," he thought, "then we shall see!"

That night, when the rats came out, Mi-ko was waiting. He stood in the middle of the floor and stared at them. First at one, then another, then at all of them at once. And the rats panicked. They squeaked and they squealed and they scrambled and tumbled. Some died of fright. Some fell trying to escape. And those that did get away never, never came back.

So Mi-ko saved the silkworms, and the old couple were never bothered by rats again. And ever since then, to this very day, Japanese silkworm farmers have put pictures of Mi-ko beside their trays of silkworms. For they know that his fierce and terrible stare will keep them safe from rats.

And so it does.

ZOOM AT SEA

by Tim Wynne-Jones

Z oom loved water. Not to drink—Zoom liked water to play with.
One night, when a leaky tap filled the kitchen sink, Zoom
strapped wooden spoons to his feet with elastic bands and paddled
in the water for hours. He loved it.

The next night he made a boat from a wicker basket with a
towel for a sail. Blown around the bathtub all night, he was as happy
as could be.

There was no stopping him. Every night when other self-
respecting cats were out mousing and howling Zoom stayed indoors
and sailed about in the dark. By day he watched the tap and dreamed.

One afternoon while dreaming in the attic he noticed a shelf he
had not seen before. A dusty diary lay next to a photograph of a
large yellow tom cat with white whiskers and a black sou'wester. It

was inscribed: "For Zoom from Uncle Roy."

Zoom opened the diary and on the last page he found an address and a map. "The Sea and how to get there," it said.

The Sea was not far, really. Zoom took a bus. He arrived very early in the morning, at a house with a big front door. It was so early Zoom was afraid to knock but the light was on and if he listened closely he thought he could hear someone inside. With great excitement he rapped three times.

The door opened. Before him stood a large woman in a blue dress. She wore silver ear-rings and many silver bracelets on her wrists.

"I want to go to sea," said Zoom nervously.

The woman smiled, but said nothing. Zoom spoke louder.

"I'm Uncle Roy's nephew and I want to go to sea."

"Ahh!" said the woman, nodding her head. "Come in, my little sailor." Inside was cold and damp.

"I am Maria," said the woman. "I'm not ready just yet." She was

busy putting her hair up in a tidy bun. The room was quiet and dark; everything was still. Far away Zoom could hear a sound like a leaky faucet.

He sat, trying to be patient, while Maria bustled around. Sometimes it was difficult to see her in the gloom, but he could hear the swish of her skirts and the tinkling of her bracelets.

The Sea was nothing like Uncle Roy had described in his diary. Zoom was sure he had made a mistake and he was just about to sneak away when Maria looked at her watch and winked.

"Now I'm ready."

And with that, she turned an enormous wheel several times to the right. The floor began to rumble and machinery began to whirr and hum. The room grew lighter and Zoom saw that it was very large.

Now Maria pushed a button and cranked a crank. Zoom could hear the sound of water rushing through the pipes. First there were only puddles but then it poured from the closets and lapped at his feet.

From rows upon rows of tiny doors Maria released sea gulls and sandpipers, pelicans and terns. From pots and cages she set free hundreds of crabs and octopi and squid who scurried this way and that across the sandy floor.

Maria laughed. Zoom laughed. This was more like it. Noise and sunlight and water, for now there was water everywhere.

Suddenly Zoom realized he could not even see the walls of this giant room. Only the sun coming up like gold, and silver fish dancing on the waves. Faraway he could see a fishing boat.

Maria smiled and said, "Go on. It's all yours."

Quickly he gathered some old logs and laced them together with seaweed. He made a raft and decorated it with shells as white as Maria's teeth.

When it was ready, he pushed and he heaved with all his might and launched the raft into the waves.

"I'm at Sea!" he called.

He danced around on his driftwood deck and occasionally cupped his paws and shouted very loudly back to shore.

"More waves," or "More Sun," or "More fish."

Waves crashed against the raft. The sun beat down. Fish leaped across the bow and frolicked in his wake.

Zoom looked back towards the shore and saw Maria. He realized, then, that he was tired. The waves subsided and the water gently began to roll towards the shore. Zoom sat and let the tide drift him back.

He sat with Maria at her little table drinking tea and eating fish fritters and watched the sun sink into the sea. As the light dimmed the room didn't seem half so big.

Maria's bun had come undone and there was sand in the ruffles at the bottom of her dress, but still she smiled and her jewellery tinkled silver in the twilight.

"Thank you for a great day," said Zoom as he stood at the door. "May I come back?"

"I'm sure you will," said Maria.

And he did.

WINTER DARK

Winter dark comes early
mixing afternoon
and night.
Soon
there's a comma of a moon,

and each streetlight
along the
way
puts its period
to the end of day.

Now
a neon sign
punctuates the dark
with a bright
blinking
breathless
exclamation mark!

Go Wind

Go wind, blow
Push wind, swoosh.
      Shake things
      take things
      make things
            fly.

      Ring things
      swing things
      fling things
         high.

Go wind, blow
Push things
wheee.
      No, wind, no
      Not me—
      not *me.*

Poems by Lilian Moore

WEATHER REPORT

Pinging rain
stinging sleet
tonight.

Frost at dawn,
bright
sun in the
morning.

Ice-bearing trees,
a glass
orchard,
blinking
sunwinking.

A noonwind will
pass,
harvesting the brittle crop,
crashing
clinking.

WINTER CARDINAL

Fat
and elegantly
crested,
clinging to the branch
of the stripped tree
like
one bright leaf that
bested
every wind and lived
to show
its red
against
the astonished snow.

Poems by Lilian Moore

GLEN LOATES

by Trudee Tomlinson

Glen Loates is a Canadian artist who paints animals, birds, and plants. His paintings are very special because the animals and plants in them look so *real*, as if they had been photographed with a magic camera. This may be because Glen has been observing nature closely since his childhood. As young boys, he and his twin brother Bernard would frequently visit the wooded areas near their home to watch the birds and small animals. He began drawing what he saw when he was six years old, using crayons and coloured pencils.

© Glen Loates

Today he uses special watercolour techniques to make his paintings realistic. For each of his pictures of large animals he uses paint, India ink, and Chinese white drawing ink to show the tiny details of the animal's fur and muscles.

Glen Loates was well known by the time he was twenty years old. His art has been the subject of several television and film documentaries and his paintings are a familiar sight on calendars and greeting cards.

But Glen Loates' interest in wildlife is more than just artistic. He is concerned about nature and donates a lot of his time to groups who want to preserve the environment. As he has travelled all over Canada to see the subjects of his paintings in their natural setting, he has grown to love the creatures and the plants that make up our natural world. Through his paintings he wants to show us the beauty of the world around us, and to warn us that if we are not careful we could lose it forever.

© Glen Loates

from

STONE FOX

by John Reynolds Gardiner

Little Willie lives with his grandfather on a farm. His grandfather is sick and cannot work, and the farm is going to be taken away from him unless Willie can raise five hundred dollars to pay the taxes. Willie uses all his savings to enter a dogsled race in town. To win the first prize of five hundred dollars, Willie and his dog Searchlight must beat the legendary Indian racer Stone Fox, who has never lost a race.

The day of the race arrived.

After adding some wood to the fire, little Willy kissed Grandfather, hitched up Searchlight, and started off for town.

At the edge of their property he stopped the sled for a moment and looked back at the farmhouse. The roof was covered with freshly fallen snow. A trail of smoke escaped from the stone chimney. The jagged peaks of the Teton Mountains shot up in the background toward the clear blue sky overhead. "Yes, sir," he remembered Grandfather saying. "There are some things in this world worth dying for."

Little Willy loved this country. He loved to hike and to fish and to camp out by a lake. But he did not like to hunt. He loved animals too much to be a hunter.

He had killed a bird once with a slingshot. But that had been when he was only six years old. And that had been enough. In fact, to this day, he still remembered the spot where the poor thing was buried.

Lost in his thoughts, little Willy got to town before he knew it. As he turned onto Main Street, he brought the sled to an abrupt halt.

He couldn't believe what he saw.

Main Street was jammed with people, lined up on both sides of the street. There were people on rooftops and people hanging out of windows. Little Willy hadn't expected such a big turnout. They must have all come to see Stone Fox.

Searchlight pulled the sled down Main Street past the crowd. Little Willy saw Miss Williams, his teacher, and Mr. Foster from the bank, and Hank from the post office. And there were Doc Smith and Mayor Smiley. The city slickers were there. And even Clifford Snyder, the tax man, was there. Everybody.

Lester came out of the crowd and walked alongside little Willy for a while. It was one of the few times little Willy had ever seen Lester without his white apron.

"You can do it, Willy. You can beat him," Lester kept saying over and over again.

They had a race for the youngsters first, and the crowd cheered and rooted for their favourites. It was a short race. Just down to the end of Main Street and back. Little Willy didn't see who won. It didn't matter.

And then it was time.

The old church clock showed a few minutes before ten as the contestants positioned themselves directly beneath the long banner that stretched across the street. They stood nine abreast. Stone Fox in the middle. Little Willy right next to him.

Little Willy had read all about the other contestants in the newspaper. They were all well-known mountain men with good racing records and excellent dog teams. But, even so, all bets were on Stone Fox. The odds were as high as a hundred to one that he'd win.

Not one cent had been bet on little Willy and Searchlight.

"What happened to Willy's eye?" Doc Smith asked Lester.

"Bumped it this morning when he got up, he told me. Just nervous. Got a right to be." Lester was chewing on his hand, his eyes glued on Stone Fox. "Big Indian," he whispered to himself.

Although little Willy's eye was black, puffy, and swollen shut, he still felt like a winner. He was smiling. Searchlight knew the route as well as he did, so it really didn't matter if he could see at

all. They were going to win today and that was final. Both of them knew it.

Stone Fox looked bigger than ever standing next to little Willy. In fact, the top of little Willy's head was dead even with Stone Fox's waist.

"Morning, Mr. Stone Fox," little Willy said, looking practically straight up. "Sure's a nice day for a race."

Stone Fox must have heard little Willy, but he did not look at him. His face was frozen like ice, and his eyes seemed to lack that sparkle little Willy remembered seeing before.

The crowd became silent as Mayor Smiley stepped out into the street.

Miss Williams clenched her hands together until her knuckles turned white. Lester's mouth hung open, his lips wet. Mr. Foster

began chewing his cigar. Hank stared without blinking. Doc Smith held her head up proudly. Clifford Snyder removed a gold watch from his vest pocket and checked the time.

Tension filled the air.

Little Willy's throat became dry. His hands started to sweat. He could feel his heart thumping.

Mayor Smiley raised a pistol to the sky and fired.

The race had begun!

Searchlight sprang forward with such force that little Willy couldn't hang on. If it weren't for a lucky grab, he would have fallen off the sled for sure.

In what seemed only seconds, little Willy and Searchlight had travelled down Main Street, turned onto North Road, and were gone. Far, far ahead of the others. They were winning. At least for the moment.

Stone Fox started off dead last. He went so slowly down Main Street that everyone was sure something must be wrong.

Swish! Little Willy's sled flew by the schoolhouse on the outskirts of town, and then by the old deserted barn.

Swish! Swish! Swish! Other racers followed in hot pursuit.

"Go, Searchlight! Go!" little Willy sang out. The cold wind pressed against his face, causing his good eye to shut almost completely. The snow was well packed. It was going to be a fast race today. The fastest they had ever run.

The road was full of dangerous twists and turns, but little Willy did not have to slow down as the other racers did. With only one dog and a small sled, he was able to take the sharp turns at full speed without risk of sliding off the road or losing control.

Therefore, with each turn, little Willy pulled further and further ahead.

Swish! The sled rounded a corner, sending snow flying. Little Willy was smiling. This was fun!

About three miles out of town the road made a half circle around a frozen lake. Instead of following the turn, little Willy took a short-cut right across the lake. This was tricky going, but Searchlight had done it many times before.

Little Willy had asked Mayor Smiley if he was permitted to go across the lake, not wanting to be disqualified. "As long as you leave town heading north and come back on South Road," the mayor had said, "anything goes!"

None of the other racers attempted to cross the lake. Not even Stone Fox. The risk of falling through the ice was just too great.

Little Willy's lead increased.

Stone Fox was still running in last place. But he was picking up speed.

At the end of five miles, little Willy was so far out in front that he couldn't see anybody behind him when he looked back.

He knew, however, that the return five miles, going back into town, would not be this easy. The trail along South Road was practically straight and very smooth, and Stone Fox was sure to close the gap. But by how much? Little Willy didn't know.

Doc Smith's house flew by on the right. The tall trees surrounding her cabin seemed like one solid wall.

Grandfather's farm was coming up next.

When Searchlight saw the farmhouse, she started to pick up speed. "No, girl," little Willy yelled. "Not yet."

As they approached the farmhouse, little Willy thought he saw someone in Grandfather's bedroom window. It was difficult to see with only one good eye. The someone was a man. With a full beard.

It couldn't be. But it was! It was Grandfather!

Grandfather was sitting up in bed. He was looking out the window.

Little Willy was so excited he couldn't think straight. He started to stop the sled, but Grandfather indicated no, waving him on. "Of course," little Willy said to himself. "I must finish the race. I haven't won yet."

"Go, Searchlight!" little Willy shrieked. "Go, girl!"

Grandfather was better. Tears of joy rolled down little Willy's smiling face. Everything was going to be all right.

And then Stone Fox made his move.

One by one he began to pass the other racers. He went from last place to eighth. Then from eighth place to seventh. Then from seventh to sixth. Sixth to fifth.

He passed the others as if they were standing still.

He went from fifth place to fourth. Then to third. Then to second. Until only little Willy remained.

But little Willy still had a good lead. In fact, it was not until the last two miles of the race that Stone Fox got his first glimpse of little Willy since the race had begun.

The five Samoyeds looked magnificent as they moved effortlessly across the snow. Stone Fox was gaining, and he was gaining fast. And little Willy wasn't aware of it.

Look back, little Willy! Look back!

But little Willy didn't look back. He was busy thinking about Grandfather. He could hear him laughing . . . and playing his harmonica . . .

Finally little Willy glanced back over his shoulder. He couldn't believe what he saw! Stone Fox was nearly on top of him!

This made little Willy mad. Mad at himself. Why hadn't he looked back more often? What was he doing? He hadn't won yet. Well, no time to think of that now. He had a race to win.

"Go, Searchlight! Go, girl!"

But Stone Fox kept gaining. Silently. Steadily.

"Go, Searchlight! Go!"

The lead Samoyed passed little Willy and pulled up even with Searchlight. Then it was a nose ahead. But that was all. Searchlight moved forward, inching *her* nose ahead. Then the Samoyed regained the lead. Then Searchlight . . .

When you enter the town of Jackson on South Road, the first buildings come into view about a half a mile away. Whether Searchlight took those buildings to be Grandfather's farmhouse again, no one can be sure, but it was at this time that she poured on the steam.

Little Willy's sled seemed to lift up off the ground and fly. Stone Fox was left behind.

But not that far behind.

The crowd cheered madly when they saw little Willy come into view at the far end of Main Street, and even more madly when they saw that Stone Fox was right on his tail.

"Go, Searchlight! Go!"

Searchlight forged ahead. But Stone Fox was gaining!

"Go, Searchlight! Go!" little Willy cried out.

Searchlight gave it everything she had.

She was a hundred feet from the finish line when her heart burst. She died instantly. There was no suffering.

The sled and little Willy tumbled over her, slid along the snow for a while, then came to a stop about ten feet from the finish line. It had started to snow—white snowflakes landed on Searchlight's

dark fur as she lay motionless on the ground.

The crowd became deathly silent.

Lester's eyes looked to the ground. Miss Williams had her hands over her mouth. Mr. Foster's cigar lay on the snow. Doc Smith started to run out to little Willy, but stopped. Mayor Smiley looked shocked and helpless. And so did Hank, and so did the city slickers, and so did Clifford Snyder, the tax man.

Stone Fox brought his sled to a stop alongside little Willy. He stood tall in the icy wind and looked down at the young challenger, and at the dog that lay limp in his arms.

"Is she dead, Mr. Stone Fox? Is she dead?" little Willy asked, looking up at Stone Fox with his one good eye.

Stone Fox knelt down and put one massive hand on Searchlight's chest. He felt no heartbeat. He looked at little Willy, and the boy understood.

Little Willy squeezed Searchlight with all his might. "You did real good, girl. Real good. I'm real proud of you. You rest now. Just rest." Little Willy began to brush the snow off Searchlight's back.

Stone Fox stood up slowly.

No one spoke. No one moved. All eyes were on the Indian, the one called Stone Fox, the one who had never lost a race, and who now had another victory within his grasp.

But Stone Fox did nothing.

He just stood there. Like a mountain.

His eyes shifted to his own dogs, then to the finish line, then back to little Willy, holding Searchlight.

With the heel of his moccasin Stone Fox drew a long line in the snow. Then he walked back over to his sled and pulled out his rifle.

Down at the end of Main Street, the other racers began to appear. As they approached, Stone Fox fired his rifle into the air. They came to a stop.

Stone Fox spoke.

"Anyone crosses this line—I shoot."

The town looked on in silence as little Willy, carrying Searchlight, walked the last ten feet and across the finish line.

JOIN-IN RHYMES

TWITTER WHOO

The owl among the bushes sat,
The rain was soaking through his hat.
But when it dried, he said, "Oh quash,
It's all the better for the wash."
Twitter whoo, twitter whoo,
We'll do as other people do.

The owl perched on a mossy wall,
And soon began to hoot and call.
The moon appeared, he flapped his wing,
He said, "She comes to hear me sing."
Twitter whoo, twitter whoo,
We'll do as other people do.

The owl stood in the dark of night,
There was no other thing in sight.
He said, "There's nothing here to do,
Except to twitter and to whoo."
Twitter whoo, twitter whoo,
We'll do as other people do.

GRANDFATHER FROG

A Grandfather Frog sat down on a stone.
  Gunk-gunk-gunk.
Croaking a song, he sat there alone.
  Gunk-gunk-gunk.
Along came a fly and said, "Mister Frog,
Hop over and catch me, here on my log."
  Gunk-gunk-gunk.
But Grandfather Frog just sat on his stone.
  Gunk-gunk-gunk.
Thinking and croaking, he sat there alone.
  Gunk-gunk-gunk.
So the foolish young fly flew away from his log,
And was caught on the tongue of Grandfather Frog.
  Gunk-gunk-gunk.

THE MISCHIEVOUS RAVEN

A farmer went trotting upon his grey mare,
  Bumpety, bumpety, bump!   (BUMPILY)
With his daughter behind him, so rosy and fair,
  Lumpety, lumpety, lump!   (GAILY)
A raven cried "Croak," and they all tumbled down,
  Bumpety, bumpety, bump!   (DESCENDING TONES)
The mare broke her knees, and the farmer his crown,
  Lumpety, lumpety, lump!   (SADLY)
The mischievous raven flew laughing away,
  Bumpety, bumpety, bump!   (LAUGHINGLY)
And vowed he would serve them the same the next day.
  Lumpety, lumpety, lump!   (MISCHIEVOUSLY)

Acknowledgements

The Marvellous Inventions of Alvin Fernald: By permission of Holt, Rinehart and Winston. *The Tiger-Skin Rug:* Reprinted by permission of Faber and Faber Ltd from THE TIGER-SKIN RUG by Gerald Rose. *Dinner at Alberta's:* Entire text and 5 specified illustrations from DINNER AT ALBERTA'S by Russell Hoban, Pictures by James Marshall (Thomas Y. Crowell Co.) Text Copyright © 1975 by Russell Hoban. Pictures Copyright © 1975 by James Marshall. By permission of Harper & Row, Publishers, Inc. *Johnny the Juvenile Juggler:* From THE DENNIS LEE AND FRANK NEWFELD 1980 CALENDAR & *The Bully:* From THE DENNIS LEE AND FRANK NEWFELD 1979 CALENDAR. Reprinted by permission of Macmillan of Canada, A Division of Canada Publishing Corporation. *Can You Canoe?* JELLY BELLY © 1983 Dennis Lee. Reprinted by permission of Macmillan of Canada, A Division of Canada Publishing Corporation and Blackie and Son Ltd. U.K. *Mountain Rose:* By Patti Stren. Copyright © 1982 by Patti Stren. Reprinted by permission of the publisher, E.P. Dutton, a division of New American Library. *Chocolate Fever:* Excerpt reprinted by permission of Coward-McCann from CHOCOLATE FEVER, copyright © 1972 by Robert K. Smith. *Away From Home:* Reprinted with permission of Macmillan Publishing Company from GROWN-UPS AND OTHER PROBLEMS by Peter Mayle and Arthur Robins. Copyright © Escargot Productions Ltd. 1982. *Green:* By Joe Raposo. Published by Jonico Music, Inc. © Copyright 1970, 1972. Used by permission. All rights reserved. *The Strange Story of the Frog Who Became a Prince:* Adapted from THE STRANGE STORY OF THE FROG WHO BECAME A PRINCE by Elinor Horwitz. Illustrated by John Heinly. Text copyright © 1971 by Elinor Horwitz. Illustrations copyright © 1971 by John Heinly. Reprinted by permission of DELACORTE PRESS. *Charlotte's Web:* Extract from p. 80 in CHARLOTTE'S WEB by E.B. White. Copyright 1952, 1980 by E.B. White. Reprinted by permission of Harper & Row, Publishers, Inc. *The Case of the Mysterious Tramp:* From ENCYCLOPEDIA BROWN FINDS THE CLUES by Donald J. Sobol. Copyright © 1966 by Donald J. Sobol. Reprinted by permission of E.P. Dutton, a division of New American Library. *Return to Air:* By Philippa Pearce from Philippa Pearce: WHAT THE NEIGHBOURS DID & OTHER STORIES (Puffin Books 1975) pp. 117-123. Copyright © Philippa Pearce, 1959, 1967, 1969, 1972. Reprinted by permission of Penguin Books Ltd. *Welcome & The Pocket:* By sean o huigin, reprinted from WELL, YOU CAN IMAGINE, published by Black Moss Press. *How to Get Rid of Bad Dreams:* By Nancy Hazbry and Roy Condy. Copyright © 1983 by Nancy Hazbry and Roy Condy. Reprinted by permission of Scholastic-TAB Publications, Richmond Hill, Ont. *The Tailypo:* By Joanna Galdone, illustrated by Paul Galdone. Text copyright © 1977 by Joanna Galdone. Illustration copyright © 1977 by Paul Galdone. Reprinted by permission of Clarion Books/Ticknor & Fields, a Houghton Mifflin Company. *The BFG:* By Roald Dahl, illustrated by Quentin Blake. Reprinted by permission of Jonathan Cape Ltd. *The Witch:* From NIGHTMARES by Jack Prelutsky. Copyright © 1976 by Jack Prelutsky. By permission of Greenwillow Books (A Division of William Morrow & Company). *Bunya the Witch:* © 1971 by Robert Kraus. First published by Windmill Books Inc. Reprinted by permission of SIMON & SCHUSTER, Inc. *The Witch Who Wasn't:* From THE WITCH WHO WASN'T by Jane Yolen, published by Macmillan Publishing Co., by permission of the author. *The Borrowers Afield:* Excerpted from THE BORROWERS AFIELD, copyright 1955, 1983 by Mary Norton. Reprinted by permission of Harcourt Brace Jovanovich, Inc. *The Witch and the Rainbow Cat:* Taken from FAIRY TALES by Terry Jones published by Pavilion Books Ltd., London. *The Rainbow Goblins:* By Ul de Rico. Extract from THE RAINBOW GOBLINS. Copyright Schuler Verlag 1977. English text copyright Mitchell Beazley Publishers Ltd. 1978. *Look to the Rainbow:* By E.Y. Harburg. Copyright © 1947 by Chappell & Co. Copyright renewed. International Copyright Secured. All rights reserved. Used by permission of Chappell Music Canada Limited. *If I Only Had a Brain & Over the Rainbow:* © 1938-1939 renewed 1966-1967 Metro-Goldwyn-Mayer, Inc. Assigned to CBS Catalogue Partnership. All rights controlled and administered by CBS Feist Catalogue, Inc. All rights reserved. International Copyright Secured. Used by permission. *The Magician's Nephew:* Extract from C.S. Lewis' THE MAGICIAN'S NEPHEW, reproduced by permission of The Bodley Head. *Walking, Careful Connie, Josephine Calico & Attic Fanatic:* Reprinted with permission from the book AUNTIE'S KNITTING A BABY by Lois Simmie. Published by Western Producer Prairie Books. *The Garden of Abdul Gasazi:* By Chris Van Allsburg. Copyright © 1979 by Chris Van Allsburg. Reprinted by permission of Houghton Mifflin Company. *Cloudy With a Chance of Meatballs:* By Judi Barrett. Copyright (text) © 1978 Judi Barrett. Reprinted with permission of Atheneum Publishers, Inc. *Look Through My Window:* Extract from pp. 230-231 in LOOK THROUGH MY WINDOW by Jean Little. Copyright © 1970 by Jean Little. By permission of Harper & Row, Publishers, Inc. *Taking Care of Crumley:* Reprinted by permission of Kids Can Press, Toronto. Text Copyright © 1984 by Ted Staunton. Illustrations Copyright © 1984 by Tina Holdcroft. *Tales for the Perfect Child:* 'Ruby' and 'Arthur' from TALES FOR THE PERFECT CHILD by Florence Parry Heide. Text Copyright © 1985 by Florence Parry Heide. Illustrations Copyright © 1985 by Victoria Chess. By permission of Lothrop, Lee & Shepard Books (A Division of William Morrow & Company). *Pearls, Oranges & Wars:* From HEY, WORLD, HERE I AM by Jean Little. Copyright 1986 by Jean Little. Reprinted by permission of Kids Can Press. *Louisa, Louisa:* (pp. 55-56) in KATE by Jean Little. Copyright © 1971 by Jean Little. By permission of Harper & Row, Publishers, Inc. *Tales of a Fourth Grade Nothing:* From TALES OF A FOURTH GRADE NOTHING by Judy Blume. Text copyright © 1972 by Judy Blume. Reprinted by permission of the publisher, E.P. Dutton, a division of New American Library. *Feelings:* Text and Illustrations from pages 5, 14, 22, and 31 in FEELINGS by Aliki. Copyright © 1984 by Aliki Brandenberg. By permission of Greenwillow Books (A Division of William Morrow & Company). *Who's Training Who?:* Reprinted from OWL Magazine © 1982 with permission of the publisher, The Young Naturalist Foundation. *The Games That Seem:* By permission of Patrick Lane. *My Favourite Things:* Copyright 1959 by Richard Rodgers and Oscar Hammerstein II, Williamson Music Co., owner of publication and allied rights throughout the Western Hemisphere and Japan. International Copyright Secured. All rights reserved. Used by permission of Chappell Music Canada Limited. *Gentle Ben:* From GENTLE BEN by Walt Morey. Copyright © 1965 by Walt Morey. Reprinted by permission of the publisher, E.P. Dutton, a division of New American Library. *Rikki-Tikki-Tavi:* Adapted by Bill Martin, Jr. from RIKKI TIKKI TAVI by Rudyard Kipling. Adaptation copyright © 1972 by Holt, Rinehart and Winston, Publishers. Reproduced with permission. All rights reserved. *Your Own Best Secret Place:* By Byrd Baylor and Peter Parnall, adapted from the text, YOUR OWN BEST SECRET PLACE. Copyright © 1979 by Byrd Baylor. Illustrations Copyright © 1979 Peter Parnall. Reprinted with the permission of Charles Scribner's Sons. *Poems of the Field:* Reprinted with permission of Macmillan Publishing Company from INSIDE TURTLE'S SHELL AND OTHER POEMS OF THE FIELD by Joanne Ryder. Text, Copyright © 1985 by Joanne Ryder. *The Stare of the Cat:* By Eiko Takeda. Reprinted with permission of MacDonald & Co (Publishers) Ltd. and Kodansha Ltd. *Zoom at Sea:* Written by Tim Wynne-Jones, illustrated by Ken Nutt. Published by Groundwood Books, 1983. *Winter Dark, Go Wind, Winter Cardinal, Weather Report:* By Lilian Moore, from the compilation SOMETHING NEW BEGINS. Copyright © 1982 Lilian Moore. Reprinted with the permission of Atheneum Publishers, Inc. *Glen Loates:* Illustrations from GLEN LOATES: A BRUSH WITH LIFE, published by Prentice-Hall Canada Inc. *Stone Fox:* Chapters 8-10 (slightly abridged text) from STONE FOX by John Reynolds Gardiner (Thomas Y. Crowell Co.) Text Copyright © 1980 by John Reynolds Gardiner. By permission of Harper & Row, Publishers, Inc. *The Best Christmas Pageant Ever:* Chapter 7 in THE BEST CHRISTMAS PAGEANT EVER by Barbara Robinson. Text copyright © 1972 by Barbara Robinson. By permission of Harper & Row, Publishers, Inc.